Production
Drawings

What is the Code about?

This Code is about the drawings which appear on every building site and contain the drawn information for construction. Throughout the Code they are referred to as the production drawings or collectively as the production set.

Who is the Code for?

The Code is for use by all members of the design team who have the task of preparing and issuing production drawings. It is directed at helping them to manage this task so that they can provide the necessary information in an effective and economic manner. The Code is complementary to BS 1192: 1984: 'Construction Drawing Practice'.

Why is the Code needed?

Experience shows that poor production drawings have too often been the cause of a low quality finished product, poor cost control and failure to meet completion dates. Well organised, complete and co-ordinated production drawings are a prerequisite for the proper management of construction.

Relationship with the Code for Project Specification.

The Code of Procedure for Project Specification is intended to be used in conjunction with this Code. They cover, respectively, the descriptive and graphic information produced by designers for use by builders. The two Codes have been written with a view to improving specifications and drawings and the co-ordination between them.

Relationship with SMM7.

This Code sets out the SMM7 requirements for drawings to be provided at tender stage. Guidance is given on how to present tender drawings to assist the builder in producing copies for obtaining sub-contract quotations.

What backing does the Code have?

The development of the Code was overseen by the Co-ordinating Committee for Project Information as part of its work in implementing the recommendations of the Project Information Group of the NCC Standing Committee on Computing and Data Co-ordination. The Code was drafted by a Drawings Working Group (See Appendix 1) set up by CCPI's four sponsoring bodies, the Royal Institute of British Architects, Royal Institution of Chartered Surveyors, Association of Consulting Engineers and Building Employer's Confederation, who have formally approved the Code and recommend its use.

The support of the Department of the Environment in preparing this Code is greatly appreciated.

Production Drawings

A code of procedure for building works

Co-ordinated project information

First edition, December 1987

Published by the Building Project Information Committee

Copyright   Association of Consulting Engineers
© 1987   Building Employers Confederation
             Royal Institute of British Architects
             The Royal Institution of Chartered Surveyors

ISBN 0 9512662 1 7

Figures and diagrams prepared by John Birch

Set and printed by NBS Services Ltd, Newcastle upon Tyne

Contents

Abbreviations

ACE	Association of Consulting Engineers
BEC	Building Employers Confederation
BRE	Building Research Establishment
BS	British Standard
BSRIA	Building Services Research and Information Association
CAWS	Common arrangement of work sections for building works
CAD	Computer Aided Design
CCPI	Co-ordinating Committee for Project Information
CI/SfB	Construction Index Samarbetskommiten for Byggnadsfragor
CP	British Standard Code of Practice
ISO	International Organisation for Standardisation
NCC	National Consultative Council
PIG	Project Information Group of the NCC
RIBA	Royal Institute of British Architects
RICS	Royal Institution of Chartered Surveyors
SMM	Standard Method of Measurement of Building Works

Foreword

The Co-ordinated Project Information Initiative

It has long been appreciated that when the information provided to contractors is insufficient, conflicting or incorrect, this leads to problems on site with a consequent reduction in the quality of the work, delays and increased costs. The government sponsored Project Information Group (PIG) identified the trends and difficulties in 1979 and recommended the action which should be taken to effect an improvement. The Co-ordinated Project Information (CPI) initiative by the Industry followed; to extend, clarify and simplify the national conventions used in communication between designers and contractors. The initiative has been sponsored by ACE, BEC (formerly NFBTE), RIBA and RICS and represents a unique working together of builders, architects, quantity surveyors, structural and services engineers over a period of over six years. Annual approval has been obtained from the four Institutions to advance, stage by stage and the final documents have taken into account the many comments received following publication of drafts in 1984.

Financial support has come from the Department of the Environment in the form of commissioned studies, effort in kind by BRE and support for the launch of CPI. Further finance has come from the four Sponsoring Bodies for the administration of the operation and more commissioned studies, but the majority of the effort has been on a voluntary basis by representatives of the four disciplines.

The Co-ordinating Committee for Project Information, having now completed its work, is confident that if the conventions are followed they will contribute to better planned projects leading to more expeditious construction at lower cost and with better quality control. The potential for improved performance will, however, be dependent upon the willingness of those who commission buildings to allow the deployment of adequate resources at the design stage for the preparation of the necessary full and properly co-ordinated documentation.

I am glad to have this opportunity to express my thanks to all those who have so willingly contributed their time and experience towards the completion of this major initiative.

24 April 1987

Alex Gordon
Chairman, CCPI

1 Introduction

1.1 General

This Code is about the drawings which appear on every building site and contain the drawn information for construction. Throughout the Code they are referred to as the production drawings or collectively as the production set and include those drawings produced post tender by specialists and sub-contractors.

Experience shows that poor production drawings have too often been the cause of a low quality finished product, poor cost control and failure to meet completion dates. Well organised, complete and co-ordinated production drawings are a prerequisite for the proper management of construction.

The Code deals with the management of the preparation, co-ordination and issue of sets of drawings and is complementary to BS 1192: 1984 'Construction Drawing Practice' which is mainly concerned with the presentation of drawings. It is based on many years of work in research organisations, in particular that carried out at the Building Research Establishment in the 1970's, and also draws on developments in both public and private practice and the practical experience of many designers and contractors. It is intended for those who have the task of preparing and issuing production drawings and is directed at helping them to manage this work so that they can provide the necessary information in an effective and economic manner.

The Code can be used with any form of tendering or contractual procedure including those which enable building work to commence on site at an early stage. The principles are applicable when the plan of work stages are sequential or when some stages overlap so that parallel working by design team members reduces the pre-contract period. It is equally suitable for new building or work in existing buildings. In using the Code, it is important to adopt a clear plan of work acceptable to all disciplines (see example given in Appendix 2).

An effective set of production drawings cannot be produced simply by following a single, well tried routine. Guidance must consist of firm advice, some guidelines and discussion of options. For every new project, decisions have to be taken about matters such as co-ordination, arrangement, format and content of the production set. Many of the decisions can only be made in the light of the particular circumstances and the Code is designed to assist in making those decisions and to show how these fit into a programme for preparing and issuing the drawings set. In addition, the drawn information needed at tender stage is listed.

1.2 The Common Arrangement

An important element of the CCPI co-ordinating function has been the development of a common arrangement for specifications and bills of quantities. Although primarily designed for specifications and bills of quantities, consideration has been given to its suitability for the arrangement of drawings.

Any widely applicable scheme for the arrangement of drawings must have sufficient flexibility to cater for the many different types of building project. This is in marked contrast to the arrangement of specifications and quantities, in which a high degree of standardisation is both practicable and desirable. Specifications and quantities describe and quantify each type of work in a project under standard headings e.g. brickwork, steelwork, concrete cladding, windows, etc. Drawings, among other things, show the size, shape and relationships between the various types of work, which vary significantly project to project, and this has a strong influence on their arrangement.

Some drawings are conceived primarily to show just one type of work, but many others, particularly the architect's drawings, show many types of work and many relationships. Such drawings cannot be neatly parcelled into standard, definitive categories; a certain 'approximateness' has to be accepted in their classification. Thus a drawing titled 'Roof' is unlikely to show every item of information about the roof, nor will it show just the roof, for the relationships with adjacent elements and types of work are of central importance. It is clear therefore that drawn information does not lend itself to division into standard sets of mutually exclusive categories.

By contrast the 'Common arrangement of work sections' (CAWS), is conceived as a precise classification; one of its main advantages is that the categories are definitive (supported by lists of inclusions and exclusions), mutually exclusive, and virtually standard project to project. If drawings were to be arranged by CAWS, the common titling and coding between drawings, specification and quantities would be largely misleading, for the content of the drawings would almost certainly not coincide with the content of the corresponding sections of the specification and quantities. It is therefore concluded that it would not be useful to arrange drawings in accordance with CAWS.

However the contents of drawings, specifications and bills of quantities can be co-ordinated effectively without common arrangement of the drawings. For example where the content of a drawing coincides with that of a work section the CAWS title should be reflected in the drawing title. This will apply particularly to component drawings. Also the annotation of drawings with cross-reference to the project specification and bills of quantities should use the CAWS numbering, e.g. Concrete mix E10/104, Lead flashing H71, Post and rail fencing Q40/230.

1.3 Computer draughting

The number of offices using computer aided design (CAD) is increasing. CAD covers all uses of a computer for design, including computer draughting, which is the aspect relevant to this Code.

The capabilities and likely future effects of computer draughting have been kept in mind throughout the writing of the Code and, where decisions might be affected by the use of computer draughting, this is noted. These occasions are few, since most of the decisions involved in drawings production have little dependence upon the means used to draw the lines. Computer prepared drawings in most cases look like well drawn and annotated manually prepared drawings.

The way in which a computer draughting system stores its input affects the types of drawing it can readily produce. All systems can readily produce complete drawings in the form, for instance, of standard details and some systems which 'model' the building at full size in something approaching full three dimensions are capable of producing views from many angles. Systems which work only in two dimensions reproduce two dimensional 'layers' and as traditionally most information is input in plan form, it is common for only plan views at various scales to be produced and for other orientations to be drawn manually. Whilst most of the systems can cope with any geometric shape, the time taken to draw the shapes varies. The result is that, in most cases, roughly the same time is required to prepare and produce an original drawing by computer as it would take to prepare and produce it manually. However, a major benefit of computer draughting is that information can be stored in 'layers' which can be recalled instantly in different combinations. This enables the preparation of drawings which, by manual methods, would at best have required the extensive use of copy negatives or, quite often, would require additional draughting. It is also much easier to make amendments, a common source of error in manually prepared drawings.

Before there are any further significant advances in computer technology that affect the process of preparing drawings, greater use of existing technology can be expected. However, the requirements for drawings are unlikely to change until contractual and other relationships between clients, designers and constructors change. Whilst already technically possible, the day of drawings being 'wired' from the design office to the site office is still some distance away. By then the role of the drawing as a means of communication will probably have changed so much that this Code will need revision. In the meantime, the production drawing will remain a major means of communication between designers and constructors.

2 Co-ordination of information on drawings

2.1 General

This section describes the actions needed to achieve co-ordination of drawn information and relates them to project type and office organisation.

A set of production drawings comprises output from a variety of sources. The designers and technicians involved are often separated geographically and will have different backgrounds of knowledge and practice. Good communication between them is vital to the smooth running of any project.

It is common for each design group contributing to a project to produce its own separate sets of drawings in virtual isolation from the other groups. In these circumstances positive steps must be taken to co-ordinate the technical content of the various sets of drawings. It is important to be aware that co-ordination cannot be left to the production drawings stage.

To enable the technical co-ordination of information to be achieved it is also necessary for the various members of the 'design team' to have compatible terms and conditions of engagement, preferably based on an agreed plan of work. Any co-ordination responsibilities should be clearly defined in the terms of engagement.

Research has identified numerous problems which arise on site as a result of poor co-ordination and these are summarised in Figure 1.

Ways of avoiding these problems have been developed through experience and substantiated by research. Consequently, many of the more prominent co-ordination problems, and particularly those involving differences between and within architects' and structural engineers' drawings can be avoided simply through routine management of the preparation of drawings. However, co-ordination of services both with the building structure and with other services will often require special attention. On large or complex projects various techniques may need to be used in one overall co-ordination strategy.

2.2 Co-ordination strategy

Co-ordination of drawn information requires the commitment of all those involved in a project, whether producers or users of information. A clear strategy must be decided upon as early as possible in the development of a project and the relevant responsibilities defined and agreed by the design team since whatever strategy is chosen is likely to influence the subsequent design stages.

There are four activities which need attention in the development of an effective co-ordination strategy:

- Design
- Communication within the design team
- Management of drawings preparation
- Communication with drawings users

These are described below. Not all the actions relating to them will be relevant on all projects but none should be discarded without good reason.

Design

Co-ordination problems can be minimised by careful consideration at design stage of the constructional implications of the design. However it is in the design of space for services that most benefit can be derived from a good co-ordination strategy.

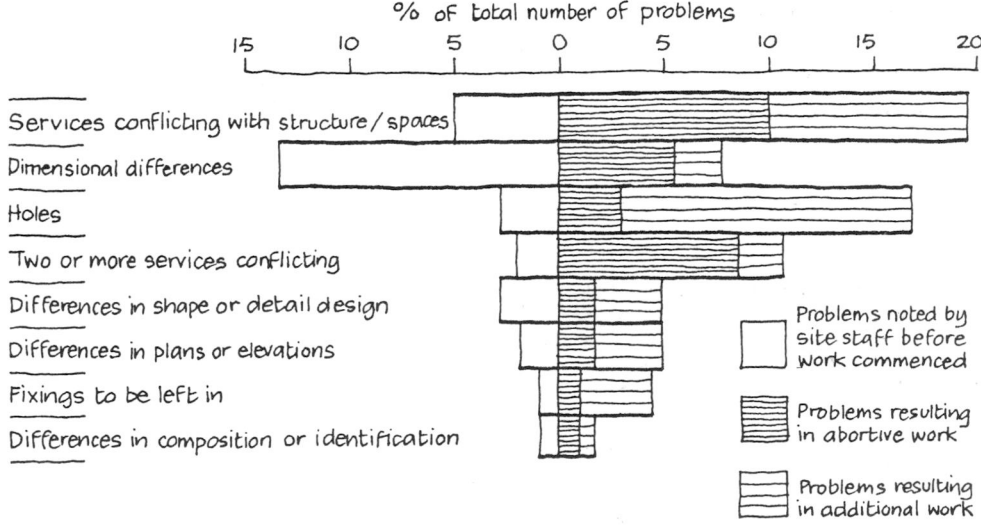

Figure 1 – The causes and effects of poor co-ordination
(from BRE CP60/76)

It is essential that the space requirements for plant and services should be settled at an early stage in the design process so that proper allowance can be made in the overall fabric design. Where possible service spaces should be divided into zones with each service being allocated a zone from which all other services are excluded. The advantage of zoning is that it allows for separate designing of individual services while taking due account of the spatial requirements of others.

Communication within the design team

Most problems result not from a complete lack of co-ordination between major building elements (e.g. between a structural system and a ventilation system) but rather between two particular components, for instance between one concrete frame member and one ventilation duct. This type of problem usually indicates poor communication between the members of the design team.

To improve communication within the design team the following procedures should be followed:

● Information passed by means of a drawing should make clear the purpose of the communication and highlight any unusual features, for instance, an unusually deep beam.
● Wherever possible, for clarity, copy negatives of the architect's drawings showing only the building outline should be used as a base for services drawings. Any additional information pertinent to the services design should be indicated on a separate marked-up print.
● Services engineers, when revising part of the services layout, must of course ensure that they are working to the architect's latest drawings.

Throughout the design and production drawing stages (see Appendix 2) it is important not only to make sure that the whole design team is aware of all changes, but that their cost and time implications both for design and construction are appreciated. Use of a proforma such as that shown in Figure 2 can greatly assist in this.

```
DESIGN VARIATION

Distribution:  Client        Struct Eng
               Architect     Services Eng
               QS

Proposed change
.....

Initiated by .....          date ...

Effect on programme
.....

Architect .....             date ...

Effect on cost
.....

Variation can/cannot be inc in BQ
QS .....                    date ...

Abortive work involved by:
.....

Fee implication .....

Decision
.....
                            date ...
```

Figure 2 – Design variation sheet
(for use during preparation of production information – initiated by whoever suggests a change and supported by a drawing where appropriate).

Management of drawings preparation

It is difficult to control the co-ordination of information on drawings if the drawings are not being prepared in an organised manner. Drawing office procedure should ensure that:

- Every production drawing is prepared with a clear and specific purpose in mind – careful arrangement of the set of production drawings will simplify this (see Sections 3 and 5).
- If copy-negatives are to be used, a plan for their production is laid down as early as possible.
- Before production drawings are started, a decision is made on a uniform pattern of scales for the various types of drawings to be produced.
- Drawing amendments are closely controlled and recorded.

Communication with drawings users

Information on drawings can become unco-ordinated simply because some decisions have not been finalised. From the user's point of view, all information on drawings can appear to have the same importance. For instance, a concrete boiler base may appear on a drawing simply as a reminder that there will be one. Its actual dimensions may not have been settled pending final selection of the boiler. Wherever possible, such information should be identified as 'provisional' and in some cases this may apply to entire drawings. An example is hole and chase drawings which can be produced to be used as consultative drawings rather than as production drawings. Site management should be made fully aware of the means which have been used to co-ordinate the drawings.

2.3 Drawings-based techniques

These techniques are particularly relevant to services work and the examples illustrate their use in that application.

Preliminary services co-ordination is carried out during the scheme design stage. Following on from the scheme design stage more detailed procedures involving special drawings-based techniques are often necessary. They include:

- Copy-negatives
- Overlay checking
- Overlay draughting
- Combined services drawings
- Detailed drawings
- Photo-drawings.

Services co-ordination for a particular project may use one or more of these. They may be applied at particular complex locations such as boiler rooms and service ducts or, if the services are complex throughout, they may be applied to all of the building. The manual activities involved can equally well be carried out by computer-based systems although the principles remain the same.

The techniques are described below together with the circumstances in which they are most appropriate.

Copy-negatives

The careful use of copy-negatives can greatly reduce the amount of draughting effort required and reduce errors which arise from repetition of information.

Copy-negatives can be taken off at any point in the development of a drawing. To minimise draughting work and to ensure that the correct amount of information appears on each copy, it is necessary to prepare a plan for the production of copy-negatives. A production plan is particularly worthwhile where an office has a workload of a particular type of building. The plan can then be used as a standard approach.

The plan should identify:
- The basic content of the master negatives
- The information to be added to the master negatives before development into a particular type of drawing
- The particular type of drawings which can be produced using a copy-negative as a base.

A typical example of a copy-negatives production plan is shown in Figure 3. (The diagram should not be seen as a model approach but merely one which is applicable to a project requiring the drawings illustrated.)

Overlay checking

After each services layout has been drawn on the architect's copy-negative, which will have been co-ordinated with structural requirements, a co-ordination meeting is held at which the relevant drawings are compared on a light table and any clashes noted. The design changes necessary to overcome these are agreed, the drawings are modified accordingly and the design is 'frozen'.

Overlay draughting

A similar but more sophisticated and flexible method is to use overlay draughting which is a technique similar to that used by cartoon animators. A set of basic location drawings is produced as above but on polyester film located with a very high degree of accuracy on a standard register or pin-bar. Copies of these location drawings are worked over by the other designers, creating their own layers of information. Any combination of layers can be checked for clashes without the need of a light table, accuracy being assured by the dimensionally stable polyester film and precise registering of the standard pin-bar. Further layers can be superimposed at any time during this process.

Single drawings can be printed by any of the usual processes but composites of around 4 layers are best reproduced on 'flat-bed' photographic or dyeline machines. More sophisticated photographic techniques are available so that there are virtually no limits to the number of layers that can be clearly reproduced as a single print. Once again upon agreement the design is 'frozen'.

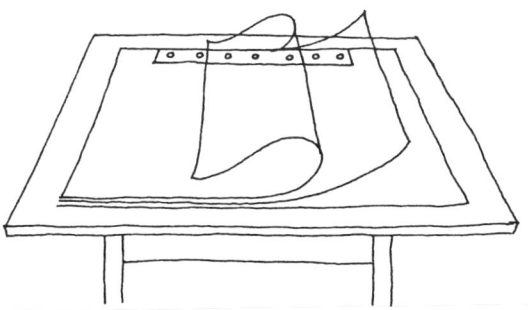

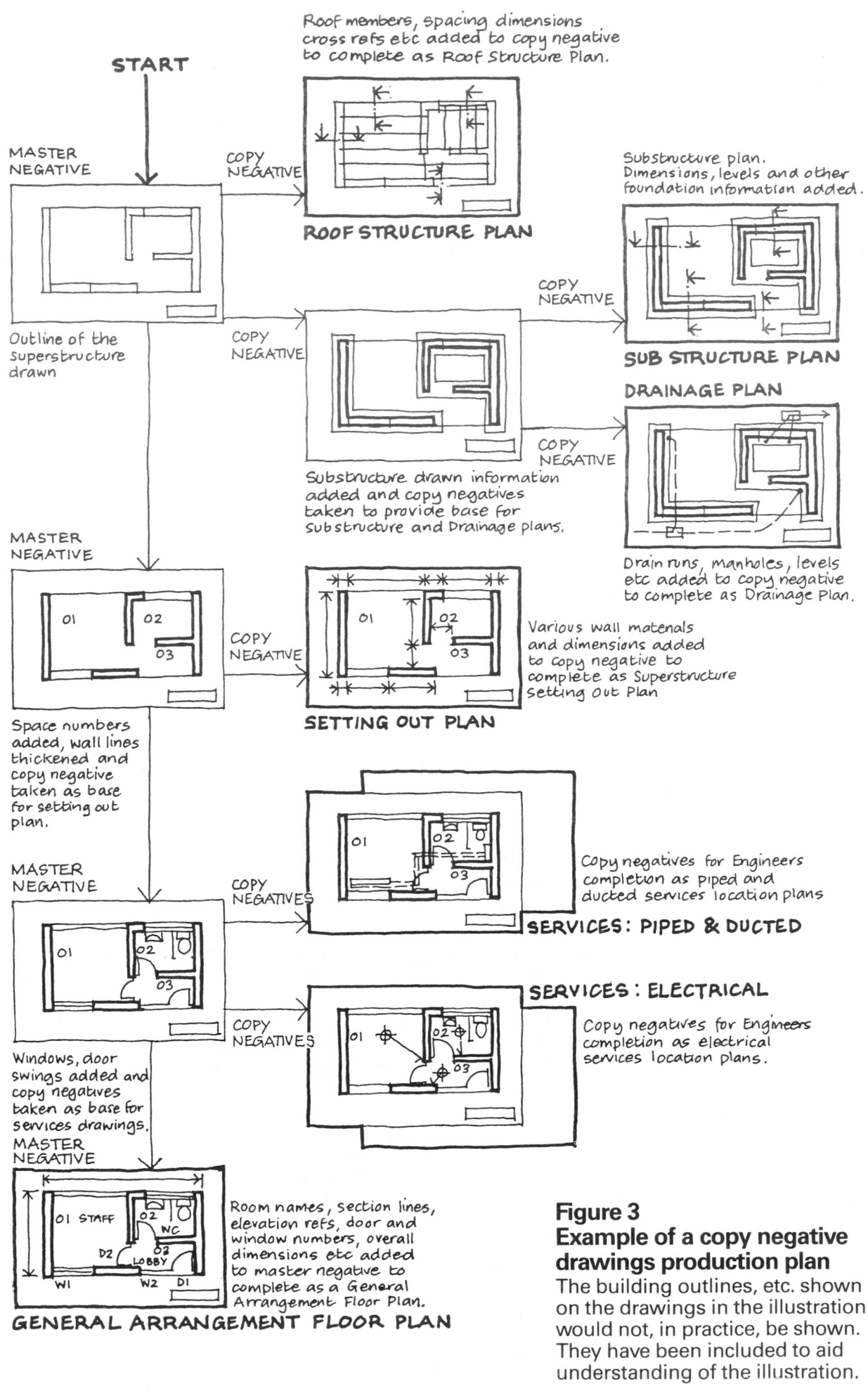

START

MASTER NEGATIVE

Outline of the Superstructure drawn

COPY NEGATIVE

Roof members, spacing dimensions cross refs etc added to copy negative to complete as Roof Structure Plan.

ROOF STRUCTURE PLAN

Substructure plan. Dimensions, levels and other foundation information added.

COPY NEGATIVE

SUB STRUCTURE PLAN

COPY NEGATIVE

Substructure drawn information added and copy negatives taken to provide base for Substructure and Drainage plans.

DRAINAGE PLAN

COPY NEGATIVE

Drain runs, manholes, levels etc added to copy negative to complete as Drainage Plan.

MASTER NEGATIVE

01   02
      03

COPY NEGATIVE

01   02
      03

Various wall materials and dimensions added to copy negative to complete as Superstructure Setting Out Plan

SETTING OUT PLAN

Space numbers added, wall lines thickened and copy negative taken as base for setting out plan.

MASTER NEGATIVE

01   02
      03

COPY NEGATIVES

01   02
      03

Copy negatives for Engineers completion as piped and ducted services location plans

SERVICES: PIPED & DUCTED

COPY NEGATIVES

01   02
      03

SERVICES: ELECTRICAL

Copy negatives for Engineers completion as electrical services location plans.

Windows, door swings added and copy negatives taken as base for services drawings.

MASTER NEGATIVE

01 STAFF   02 WC
D2   02 LOBBY
W1   W2   D1

Room names, section lines, elevation refs, door and window numbers, overall dimensions etc added to master negative to complete as a General Arrangement Floor Plan.

GENERAL ARRANGEMENT FLOOR PLAN

Figure 3
Example of a copy negative drawings production plan
The building outlines, etc. shown on the drawings in the illustration would not, in practice, be shown. They have been included to aid understanding of the illustration.

Combined services drawings

Producing a series of drawings, each of which shows only one service, is open to the risk of amendments during the life of a project creating unco-ordinated information. The use of combined services drawings, which show all of the services on one drawing sheet, reduces the likelihood of this happening while still allowing co-ordination to be achieved. There are two ways of producing combined services drawings.

The first is the most effective and though generally applicable is particularly suitable where design team meetings can be easily arranged. A series of such meetings is held to resolve co-ordination problems and one member of the design team is appointed to prepare a set of combined services location drawings showing all services routes and equipment. Copy-negatives of this set are issued to each services specialist to develop for his own purpose.

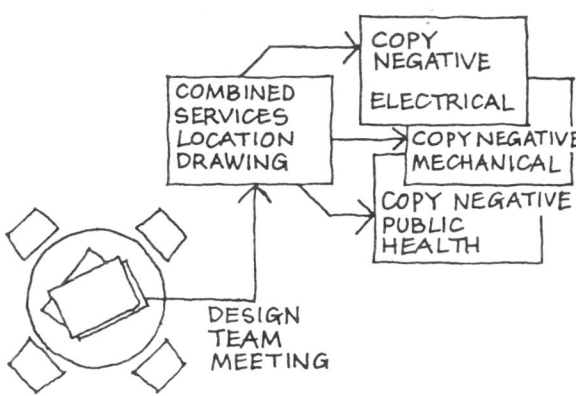

The second method can be substituted where the designers are geographically remote from each other, making frequent meetings difficult. It requires preliminary design discussions between all members of the design team at which a sequence based upon estimated relative difficulties of routing is established for designing each service. A common sequence is:

- Gravity, sanitary and rainwater pipework
- Ductwork
- Sprinkler system
- Heating pipework
- Plumbing pipework
- Electrical cables
- Controls wiring

Each services layout is added in turn onto a set of architect's location drawings which is sent to the co-ordinator, usually the architect, for approval after each addition. Any amendments required are made and approved which effectively 'freezes' the design after each step. When this process is complete copies of the resulting combined services drawings are issued to each services specialist to develop for his own purpose.

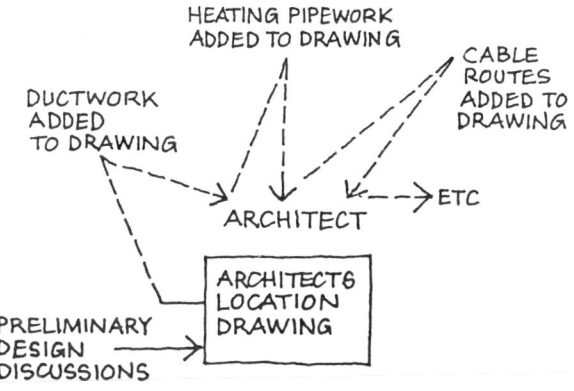

The major drawback with the sequential method is that it lacks flexibility in that the later services in the sequence have to be designed to fit in with the earlier approved service runs.

Detailed drawings

Much of the information on services location is of an indicative nature. The relationship of pipe runs, electrical conduits, ventilation ducts, etc is shown but the decision as to their precise and finally fixed positions is left largely to the installers. To ensure co-ordination, where the space available for services is limited, the information relating to them must be shown precisely. Detailed drawings provide the most satisfactory means for presenting this information. Typically, they comprise 1:20 scale sections through services corridors, rising ducts, ceiling voids, service entry points, etc.

Detailed drawings are usually used to supplement combined service location drawings by showing some of the services arrangements in the vertical plane. If comprehensive enough, they can be used as assembly drawings in their own right.

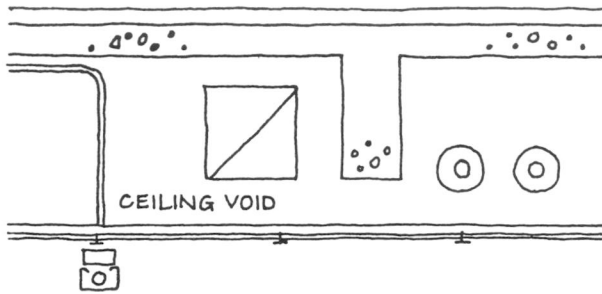

Photo drawings

If for some areas of a project comparable existing installations or suitable models are available the technique of photo-drawings can be used. A photo-drawing is an engineering assembly or location drawing which incorporates copies of photographs. These photographs show the existing installations, or the models of proposed ones, and are annotated to show such information as grid-lines, levels, dimensions, sizes and descriptions of services.

2.4 Computer draughting

The benefits of using copy negatives, overlay draughting and overlay checking can be obtained by using a computer draughting system.

Information can be stored in the system either as individual items or as 'layers' of information of particular types. At any stage in drawing production, these individual items or 'layers of information can be called up in any combination to provide complete drawings or drawings which can be used as a base for development in the same way as copy negatives. The advantage of computer draughting and overlay draughting (see page 9) is that, provided the compilation or 'layering' of the information is carefully planned, the many combinations of information available give greater flexibility in use and allow easier revision.

3 Drawings arrangement

3.1 General

The arrangement of production drawings has a major influence on user comprehension and the ability to retrieve information. This section discusses the effects of various methods of drawing arrangement, describes those which have proved most beneficial in practice and gives guidance on the choice for different types of project. Provision should be made in the chosen arrangement for those drawings produced post tender by specialists and sub-contractors.

3.2 Effects of drawings arrangement

There is no single 'best' arrangement for drawings which will apply to all projects. There are many factors such as size and complexity of project and types of construction within the project which will influence the choice: these factors are discussed in detail later in this section. The most effective arrangement will result from giving the right emphasis to each factor for the particular circumstances. The effect is shown in Figure 4 which is based on BRE research.

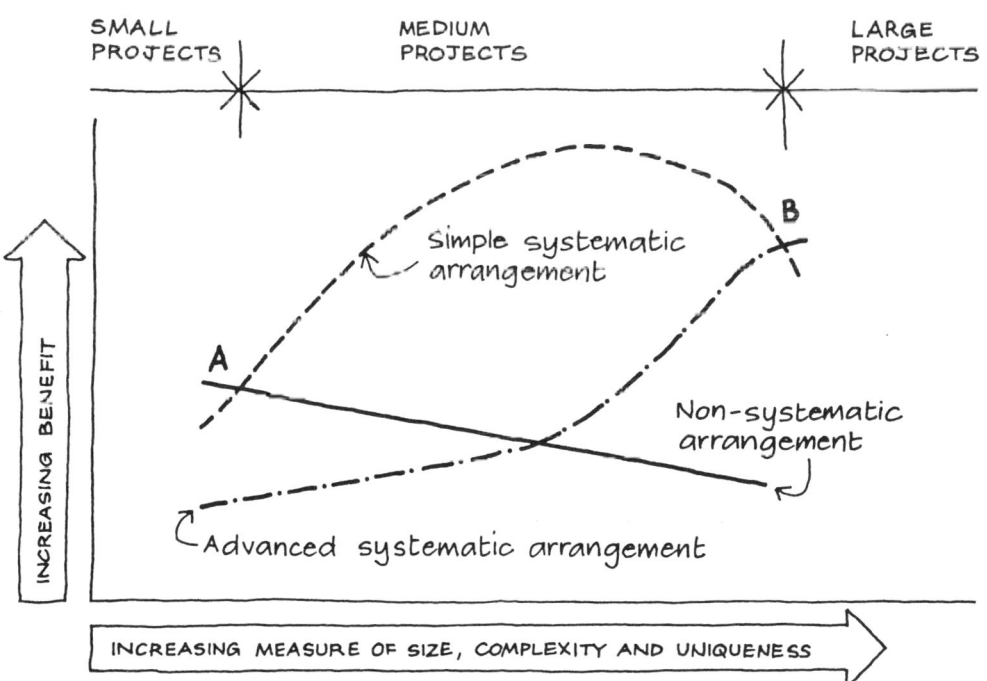

Figure 4 – The effect of drawings arrangement

The terms used in Figure 4 are defined as follows:

- *Non-systematic arrangement.*
  No groups of related drawing sheets are apparent from either the drawing numbering or the drawing types. A typical example is a set of about thirty drawings which, although their preparation may have been given some logical thought, appear as a mixture of layouts, details and schedules.

13

- *Simple systematic arrangement.*
  Groups of related drawing sheets are apparent from the drawing numbering and/or the drawing types. A typical example is a set of about a hundred drawings which is separated into location drawings, schedules, assembly drawings and component drawings.

- *Advanced systematic arrangement.*
  Initial grouping is similar to the simple systematic approach but further, more detailed division is apparent from the drawing numbering. A typical example is a set of more than two hundred and fifty drawings separated into location, co-ordination, schedule, assembly and component drawings further divided by parts of the building e.g. foundations, roof, floors.

- *Small project.*
  Typically of small to medium size and of simple construction. Requiring a minimum of information management.

- *Medium project.*
  Typically of small to medium size but complicated construction or of large size but simple construction. Requiring a fairly simple but systematic approach to information management.

- *Large project.*
  Typically of large size and complicated construction. Requiring an advanced form of information management.

A project which corresponds to changeover point A in Figure 4 might, for instance, be a hostel with a floor area of about 1,000 m^2, while one at changeover point B could be university teaching accommodation, a hospital or a building of similar complexity in excess of about 10,000 m^2 floor area.

3.3 Choice of arrangement

The essence of good arrangement is the division of the whole set of production drawings into easily recognisable groups. The choice of grouping is affected by the following factors.

Type of project

The typical small project will need no more elaborate grouping than the separation of general arrangements from details.

The typical medium project will need no more elaborate grouping than by type of information e.g. division into location, assembly and component drawings.

The typical large project will need grouping by type of information and further division by, for instance, parts of the building. Special groups such as co-ordination drawings may also be required.

Some projects will display conflicting characteristics and will be difficult to define as small, medium or large. In these cases drawings groups should be chosen to accommodate these characteristics. This means that some small projects will need grouping by type of information and some medium projects will benefit from sub-division of the assembly group. Some medium and most large projects will need grouping by zones or blocks. Projects having a variety of small units (e.g. housing sites or factory unit developments) may need grouping by unit types.

Number of drawings

Experience has shown that for groups of less than say twenty drawings, no positive structuring is necessary on grounds of comprehension or speed of retrieval of information. However, for groups of drawings greater than about twenty, sub-division is beneficial. This can mean that more elaborate grouping may be required than that suggested by the type of project. The most common occurrence is the need on a medium project to sub-divide the assembly group into parts of the building.

Design team – office practice and location

Each member of the design team tends to have a different background of experience, training and office practice and produces different types of drawings. Where the designers' offices are in close proximity to one another or they work as a multi-disciplinary team it is fairly easy to produce the drawings for a project as a fully integrated set. If their offices are far apart it can be more appropriate to make the primary grouping by 'office of origin'.

If the workload of a design office is predominantly of one building type it may be appropriate to make a standard choice of drawings arrangement. Similarly, managers of large offices may find advantages in training and supervision if a similar drawings arrangement is used for all types of project.

User needs

On any project it is useful to provide particular groups of drawings for specialist users e.g. steelwork drawings for steelwork sub-contractors. Similarly, where grouping such as parts of the building is used, its relevance to likely specialist or sub-contract work should be considered.

For any set of production drawings an order of priority for groups must be determined having given due consideration to the above factors. The most common priority is office of origin divided into:

- Type of information
- Parts of the building

The size and layout of a project will determine whether zones, unit types, etc are used as divisions of either of these categories or whether they take priority over them.

Over-fragmentation of a set of production drawings is unhelpful and should be avoided. A set of drawings may, for instance, consist of a few location and component drawings with many assembly drawings. Subdivision of the assembly drawings may be useful but subdivision of the other groups is unnecessary.

3.4 Types of drawing arrangement

In discussing choice of arrangement, various types of drawings groups have been referred to. The following groupings have been found to be most useful in practice and are discussed in this section:

- Office of origin (architect, mechanical engineer, etc)
- Type of information:
  Location (plan, section, elevation)
  Schedule
  Assembly details
  Component details
- Parts of the building (frame, walls, roof, partitions, windows, finishes, heating installation, security installation, drainage, etc) including parts constructed by specialist firms
- Location (blocks, zones, house types, levels, etc)

Grouping by office of origin

Creating drawings groups according to their office of origin has long been common practice. At its simplest, this distinguishes between architectural, structural, services and specialist contractors drawings, but on large projects any of these groups may divide naturally into smaller groups, for instance, architectural into landscape and buildings, or services into heating and lighting.

These groups arise naturally and may be identifiable through differences in draughting style as well as through the different office project numbers. The industry has been accustomed to such groupings for so long that it feels at ease with them and users on each new project quickly learn what information to expect from each of the design offices.

Disadvantages can arise from producing these groups in isolation. Co-ordination of technical content is difficult and an active policy towards co-ordination is needed.

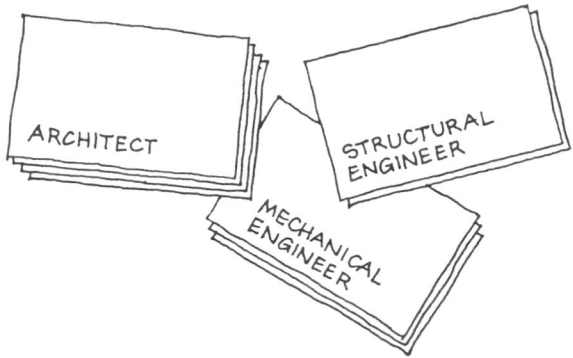

Grouping by office of origin is applicable to virtually all types of project. Usually some further grouping within one or more of the origin groups will be advantageous but on small works or works of simple design origin grouping alone may be adequate. If, for any particular project, the information emanating from each office can be shown adequately on no more than twenty sheets, further grouping is of little benefit.

In some circumstances, and particularly in the case of multi-disciplinary practices, the various designers work so closely together on individual drawings that office of origin groups are not the natural outcome. In these cases it is better to ignore this type of grouping and use one or more of the groupings which follow.

Grouping by type of information

On a very small project such as a house extension it can be both feasible and appropriate to put all of the information, including plans, sections, elevations and details, onto one drawing. On larger projects this is clearly not possible so that some separation of the building views is unavoidable. The most common way of doing this is to separate the 'general arrangement drawings' (plans, sections, elevations) from the details with the possible use of other groups, for instance schedules, as necessary.

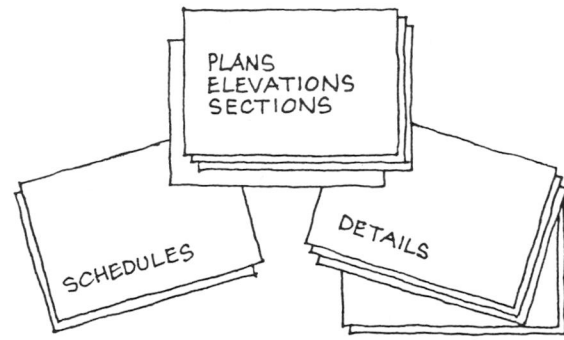

There are few problems in establishing this simple form of grouping. It gives the drawings user some assistance in information retrieval since he will often know from experience what type of information is likely to appear on what type of drawing. Nevertheless, it tends to be a rough and ready approach and will be inadequate on projects requiring large numbers of drawings.

For projects such as an office building or a school the number of drawings needed can mean that merely separating 'general arrangements' from details will not lead the user frequently enough or quickly enough to the specific information he requires. This is because the grouping does not create a clear distinction between different types of information. For instance, the position of a wall, a fixing position and a component size can all be given by a dimension. These dimensions could appear on the same type of drawing but they can more usefully be classified as different types of information: location information, assembly information and component information.

Grouping drawings in terms of these types of information can be a great aid to retrieval of information and also help the draughtsman to identify and supply more complete information.

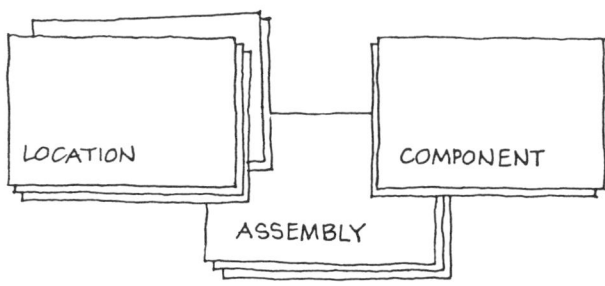

Grouping by 'type of information' means that the decisions on grouping must be taken before drawings production begins, and the drawings must then be produced to fit the chosen grouping. Nevertheless, there is considerable flexibility within the classification. Since they follow the pattern of users' searches for information it is quite acceptable for the location, assembly and component groupings to be seen as a sequence. Assembly drawings need only be produced when location drawings need amplification. Component drawings need only be produced when the assembly views are not sufficient to describe a component or separate drawings are required for manufacture.

If the flexibility of 'type of information' grouping is used to the full it is applicable to all types of project. It is most effective, however, on more complex medium size and larger projects. The discipline enforced by the grouping is a prerequisite for further, more detailed grouping which is often necessary on very large projects.

Grouping by parts of the building

On some projects, particularly large or complex ones, the number of drawings in the groups described previously can be considerable. For example, on hospital or large university projects the number of drawings in the 'assembly' group can easily number more than a hundred. In these cases, although location, assembly, component is a good initial grouping, a further grouping within one or more of these groups is advantageous.

In theory, groups based on trades, site operations or even project planning might be expected to best suit user needs. In practice, these approaches have proved too restrictive because they require designers to anticipate the contractor's construction solution. The major common factor between producers and users of drawings is the building itself so that grouping drawings by the part of the building they define has proved most effective in practice.

'Parts of the building' should only be used as a sub-grouping on projects where a 'type of information' breakdown such as location, assembly, component is worthwhile. Even then it may only be the assembly and perhaps component groups which need sub-dividing.

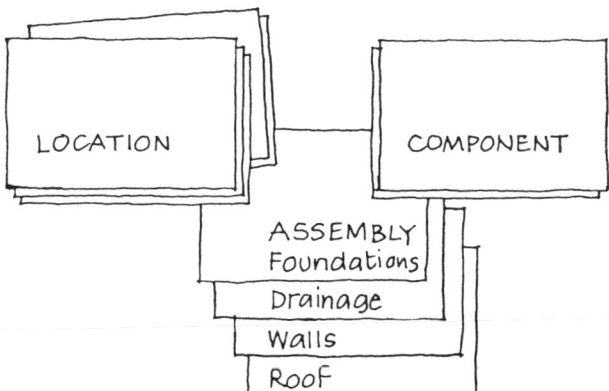

A note of warning: if a separate drawing is produced for every separate part of a building, the result can be a mass of fragmented information. This can be avoided if drawings showing several parts are grouped by reference to their predominant parts. For instance, a roof edge drawing may show information about wall, ceilings, services etc, but if the predominant information is about the roof, then it should be grouped with the roof drawings. Users soon become familiar with grouping done in this way and quickly learn the most likely whereabouts of specific information.

Grouping by parts of the building usually creates groups which relate directly to the information needs of particular users such as bricklayers, concreters etc. However, adjusting a drawings arrangement by considering the likely organisation of construction work can sometimes make drawings retrieval and use even easier.

Most projects are built by a main contractor and a number of sub-contractors. Thus there are several user firms requiring drawings. Often, grouping by office of origin will suit the main requirements of these users. For instance, an electrical sub-contractor will by-and-large require few drawings other than those from the electrical consultant. However, in some cases this relationship is not so direct and it will be advantageous to prepare sub-sets of drawings for particular sub-contractors. Examples are steelwork fabrication drawings, ventilation system drawings or, perhaps, suspended ceiling drawings.

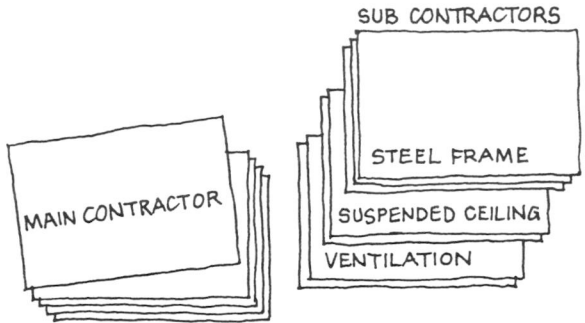

There are obvious advantages if specific groups of drawings relate only to specific users. However, apart from having the same co-ordination disadvantages as the 'office of origin' approach, it can be difficult to decide on the drawings required by a particular sub-contractor. The groupings are only really applicable if there is barely any overlap between the work of a sub-contractor and the work on the rest of the project.

Grouping by location
It is inevitable that the plans for some projects will not fit at a suitable scale onto one drawing sheet. This is often the case with large sites or large buildings. Clearly in these circumstances either the site must be split into zones or the building into appropriate blocks. As far as possible the boundaries of these zones or blocks should occur at natural construction breaks where little information is needed. They are then easily definable and the drawings for each zone or block can be grouped separately if necessary.

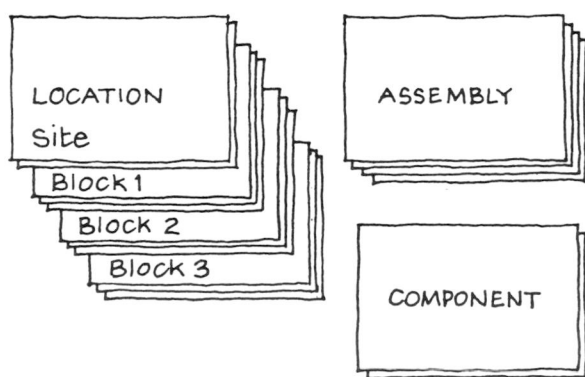

In determining the zones or blocks, factors such as appropriate sheet size, scales, etc must be taken into account as well as site layout. Once this has been done the best status for the groups so defined can be decided as follows:

- If the zones or blocks are completely or almost completely independent and have different designs, each zone or block group can be considered as if it were a separate project and sub-divided into other groups.
- If the layout of the zones or blocks differ but their detail design is similar, some other grouping (e.g. location, assembly, component) should take precedence. The zones or blocks can then form identifiable sub-groups of, say, the location drawings only.
- If some or all of the layouts of the zones or blocks are substantially the same, creating groups based on zones or blocks can cause unnecessary repetition. In these cases it is better simply to state in the title box of a drawing the zones or blocks to which it relates.

Some projects consist of layouts of similar units, for example, housing estates or factory estates. In these cases a great deal of repetition can be avoided by grouping drawings by house types or factory unit types.

4 Format of the drawings set

4.1 General

The format of a set of drawings has an important influence on the ease and convenience of its use. The choice of sheet sizes and scales can have a major effect on drawings arrangement while numbering and titling are important in ensuring that information is easily found.

4.2 Sheet sizes

General

The choice of sheet sizes should be made from the lists of preferred sizes in the ISO-A series given in BS 1192 : Part 1 : 1984 'Construction Drawing Practice'. Whatever sheet sizes are chosen for a project, it is advisable for ease of reference, storage and handling that as far as possible the sheets within any group should be of the same size.

The use of one sheet size throughout a project is often suitable but, because it enables quick and easy identification of different drawing groups, consideration should always be given to using two sizes, for instance A1 general arrangement drawings and A3 detailed drawings. The use of more than two basic sheet sizes within any one project tends to complicate methods of storage and causes inconvenience in retrieving information.

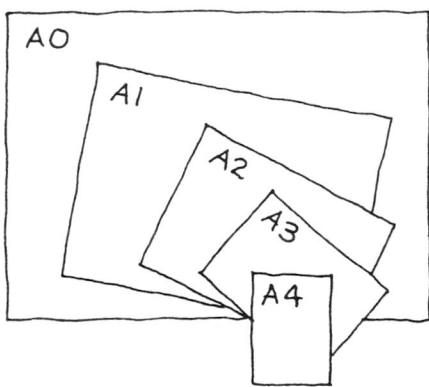

Characteristics

A0 Advantage – a large sheet which is often useful for showing large areas, such as site plans, at a generous scale. It can be produced as a one-off drawing in a set of otherwise smaller sheets.

Disadvantage – an inconvenient size for handling, storing and carrying about on site.

A1 Advantages – an easy and convenient size for handling and storing. Large enough to accept most building layouts, particularly if some thought is given to the placing of the title and information panel. If each detail or view is clearly partitioned, A1 is suitable for all types of drawings, including schedules.

Disadvantage – it is common for appropriate scale plan views of buildings of non-rectangular plan shape to fail to fit the A1 sheet. If it is desired to avoid A0 size the plan view must be split up onto separate A1 sheets, with the need for special care at the various plan boundaries.

The alternative is the use of non-preferred sheet sizes with the attendant storage problems.

A2 Advantage – suitable for detail drawings allowing flexibility in the choice of scales. Probably best used as a compromise size on projects where smaller sheets would result in fragmentation of information and larger sheets would waste paper.

Disadvantage – a rather 'in-between' size being too small to store conveniently in a plan chest or on hangers but too large to handle easily in bound book form.

A3 Advantages – the drawing space available normally allows for two large scale details. The A3 sheet size is, therefore, flexible in that, when needed, a single more extensive detail can be accommodated. This flexibility is important in enabling all the sheets in one group to be of the same size. Furthermore, the A3 size allows for a good size title and information panel and can conveniently be bound into book form when required.

Disadvantage – Care must be taken if this size is used for location or general arrangement drawings. Many buildings would require extensive zoning to fit on A3 sheets with attendant dangers of fragmentation of information.

A4 Advantages – this size is the most convenient for binding into book form and if the resultant set of A4 drawings is not too large, it can easily be carried around on site when inspecting the work. The size also allows rapid production of extra copies. These advantages can often be achieved for other basic sheet sizes by photo-reduction to A4 size.

Disadvantages – A4 size lacks flexibility, being often too small to accommodate all the building details required for a project. The small size often results in inadequate space for the title and information panels. Also extensive fragmentation of information can occur causing the user to refer to numerous sheets for information about one part of the building.

4.3 Scales

General
The choice of appropriate scales is one of the most important aspects in achieving clear, economic and accurate drawn information. The range of scales from which choices should be made is given in BS 1192: Part 1: 1984 'Construction Drawing Practice'.

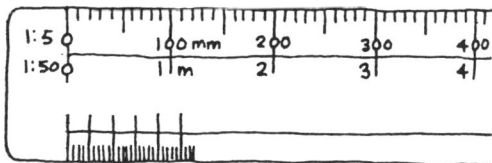

Choice of scale
The choice of scale should:

- permit easy and clear interpretation of the information which the drawing has to convey. For instance, a 1:100 plan may be ideal for general layout information and for supplying references to other more detailed drawings. However, if more detailed information is to be shown, such as brickwork setting out or the exact relationship of walls to columns, 1:50 may be preferable.
- permit easy comparison of information from different sources. For instance, plans produced by the architect, services consultant and structural consultant should, as far as possible, be to the same scale.

- be such that numerous references are not required to lead the user from small scale to large scale information. This occurs commonly when too small a scale is chosen for basic location drawings and too large a scale for details. Intermediate scale drawings then become necessary to amplify the location drawings and accommodate references to the details.
- be dictated by the clarity of information transfer rather than less important considerations. For instance, the choice of scales should not be compromised by the wish to keep all sheet sizes in the set the same or to avoid using large sheets.

4.4 Drawing numbers

General
The primary purpose of drawing numbering is to give each drawing a unique place in the set. Each drawing can then be filed and retrieved with ease.

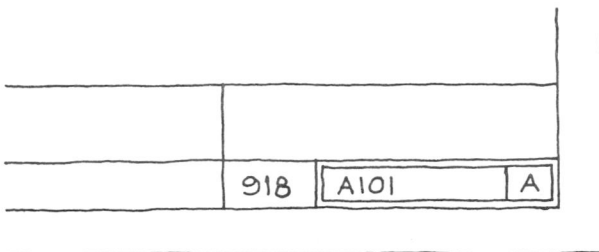

The full identification of a drawing comprises two parts; a project identification number and a drawing number. The project identification number may take a variety of forms depending on the established practice of the office of origin.

Choosing a numbering system
When choosing a numbering system, consideration should be given to the following points:

- *The number of drawings in a group or set.*
  In a small group or set of drawings, numbers assist only in filing and referencing between drawings and so need be given no special significance.

- *The drawing groupings chosen for the production set.*
  Drawing groupings are useful in searching for information only if they can be easily recognised. One way of achieving this is to identify each group by a common feature in its drawing numbers.

- *The issue of additional drawings.*
  If it is expected that extra drawings will be produced after the first issue of the set, the numbering system should allow new drawings to be slotted into their correct place in the sequence.

- *Ease of comprehension and commitment to memory.*
  An elaborate numbering system in which each number has many significant parts may be difficult to understand and easily forgotten or confused when following up references. Numbers should only be given special significance where it is of positive assistance to the user of the drawings.

Types of drawing number
- *Sequential numbers.*
  For small projects with few drawings sequential numbering is quite adequate but its lack of flexibility makes it less appropriate for sets made up of many sheets. In these larger sets, related drawings can become

widely separated in the sequence and the absence of a pattern causes difficulties in searching for information.

● *Blocks of numbers.*
The arrangement of a set should be reflected in the drawing numbering, for instance, 01 – 99 Location drawings, 100 – 199 Assembly drawings, 200 – 299 Component drawings. If any of these separate groups contains many drawings, blocks of numbers will have the same weakness as sequential numbers.

● *Mnemonic letters.*
A more readily understood method of amplifying the drawings group pattern is to add memory aids in the form of mnemonic letters to the numbering system. The most common example is the use of L, A and C to indicate location, assembly and component drawings, but there are other appropriate mnemonics such as R for reinforcement in a structural concrete set. In some cases, particularly to ensure clear distinction between drawing groups, mnemonics of more than one letter may be necessary. In a structural steelwork set CONS may indicate the group of drawings showing steelwork connection details and is thus easily distinguished from a fellow group of component drawings labelled C. Specialist contractor's drawings can also be distinguished by this method.

● *Location codes.*
Sometimes the location or general arrangement drawings relate only to one sector or zone of the building or site. If there are only a few such zones, the scope of each sheet can conveniently be identified on a small diagram in the notes column amplified by the appropriate zone name or number in the sheet title. However, the search for information on very large projects with many zones will benefit from inclusion of a suitable location code in the drawing identification number.

● *Significant codes.*
The ultimate refinement in drawing numbering is to add codes which indicate the specific subject of each sheet. This approach is only normally justified on projects large and complex enough to require sub-division of drawings by 'parts of the building'. The danger with significant codes is to allow them to influence the selection of the drawings to be produced. The result can be a proliferation of very specific drawings causing difficulties in interpretation and co-ordination. It is essential, therefore, that the decision to use significant codes should not precede decisions about drawing grouping. In most cases, whenever significant codes are used, it will also be useful to use mnemonic letters. An example is drawing numbers of the form A(21)02 where A indicates assembly drawings, (21) indicates external wall information (from CI/SfB Table 1) and 02 is a sequential number in the A(21) series.

4.5 Titling

General
The most efficient way of finding information in a drawing set is to follow up a direct drawing number reference. If no such reference is available, the search is best made by trying to identify a relevant group of drawings. Beyond this point, the drawing title is the only simple key to drawings content.

The drawings for small or uncomplicated projects may be arranged in broadly based groups or have no grouping at all. In such cases the titles take precedence in the search for information. In any set, therefore, rapid information retrieval is, to a considerable extent, dependent upon effective titling.

Effective titling should:

- achieve a balance between brevity and the comprehensive identification of the contents of the sheet;
- use consistent terminology throughout any one project. For instance, 'Staircase A' on one drawing should not become 'Staircase 1' on another drawing;
- use terminology consistent with other documents. This can be achieved by using CAWS terminology wherever appropriate.

Title content

The content of any drawing title should normally be sufficient to answer the questions:

- Where does the drawn information apply? e.g. Building A, Block B, first floor, kitchen, at eaves.
- What features does the drawing describe? e.g. brickwork, floor joists, steelwork connections, concrete bases, cold water supply.
- What type of information does the drawing convey? e.g. location, assembly, component, details, fabrication.
- What type of drawing is it? e.g. plan, elevation, isometric, schematic, schedule.

If the views on one sheet are unrelated the sheet title has to take a more general form with the more specific information supplied in a title adjacent to each view.

5 Example drawings arrangement

5.1 Introduction

The sections of this Code concerned with 'Drawings arrangement' and 'Format of the drawings set' give general guidance. This section shows how the guidance can be applied in practice by reference to a particular project. The example has been designed to illustrate the principles involved and should not necessarily be taken as typical for a project of this type.

5.2 The project

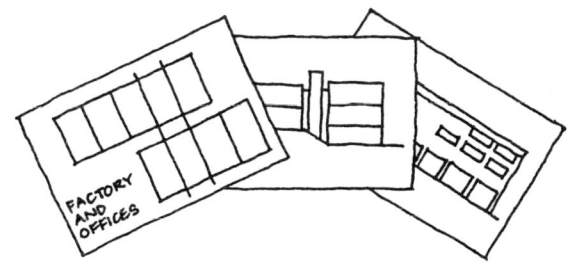

- *Generally.*
  The project comprises a three storey office building linked to a two storey factory building of the same height. The ground conditions are generally poor and the site slopes from North to South.

- *Substructure.*
  The buildings are founded on short bored piles with reinforced concrete pile caps, suspended ground floor and ground beams. The ground floor of the factory area has five reinforced concrete machine bases.

- *Frames.*
  The office building has an in situ reinforced concrete frame and the factory a steel frame with a double span lattice roof structure.

- *External Walls.*
  Both buildings have brickwork external walls up to a two metre deep pre-cast concrete panel parapet. The inner skin of the external walls is fair faced lightweight block in the factory and plastered lightweight block in the office building.

- *Internal walls/partitions.*
  Circulation space is separated from office areas by plastered block partitions. Offices are either cellular or landscaped using a demountable partition system. The partitions in the factory are fair faced blockwork.

- *Intermediate floors.*
  The office building has in situ reinforced concrete single span slabs and the factory an in situ reinforced concrete double span coffered slab.

- *Roof.*
  The office block has an in situ reinforced concrete roof slab with a screed laid to falls. The factory has a metal deck laid to falls. Both are insulated with 50 mm urethane foam and topped with a high performance built-up felt system.

- *Services.*
  The buildings have normal water supply and sanitary services as the

factory effluent is minimal. The factory process requires numerous compressed air outlets and special gas supplies. The buildings are fully air-conditioned and the office block has environmental control features such as automatic sun shades at windows and sensor controlled illumination. Other services include normal power circuits, computer links and tele-communication networks. There are two lifts and the factory has two small gantry cranes at loading bays.

- *Other features.*
  Several changes in level and the use of hidden movement joints have created the need for complicated brickwork detailing. Some of the details require special bricks. External doors and windows and the internal joinery and fittings are all purpose-made. The sloping site, the need for vehicular access to both levels of the factory and the client's requirements for an attractive, non-industrial setting have resulted in extensive external works and landscaping.

5.3 Arrangement – design team

On this project drawings are to be produced by a number of separate offices situated many miles apart. A co-ordinated approach can, therefore, only be achieved through meetings and correspondence. Integrating the drawings into a single arrangement would be difficult in these circumstances. Therefore, it is better to accept a primary grouping by office of origin but ensure co-ordination of content and format between the groups.

Decision by design team: the drawings will primarily be grouped by 'office of origin'.

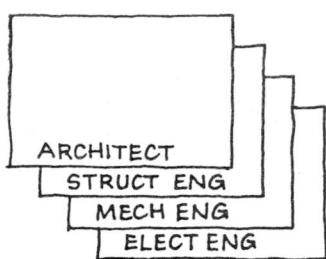

The project is about 4000 m^2 in floor area and includes a variety of construction techniques, materials and components which result in some complex detailing. It is therefore, in the terms of this Code, a 'medium' project (see page 11) which implies the need for grouping by 'type of information' e.g. location, assembly and component (see page 16).

Decision by design team: the larger 'office of origin' groups of drawings should be divided in terms of location, assembly and component information.

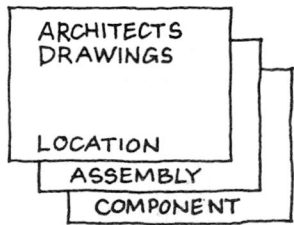

Decisions now have to be made about three interrelated matters: zoning, sheet sizes and scales. In this case they are strongly influenced by the strategy chosen for co-ordinating the design of the services and the structure. For the less heavily serviced areas of the building overlay checking is to be used which requires all floor plans to be drawn to the same scale. For the heavily serviced areas, the sequential design approach resulting in combined services drawings is to be used (see page 11). In consequence, a scale of 1:50 for floor plans is necessary.

The smallest sheet size the plans will fit on at 1:50 is A0 which is uncomfortably large. A1 is preferred. In this case the design of the building allows the convenient splitting of the plans into two zones, the office block and the factory block, and these fit easily on A1 sheets. In theory, all the drawings could be arranged in terms of those relating to the office block and those to the factory block. However, only the plans need the division into blocks and many of the detail drawings are common to both. Simply noting the relevant block in the drawing titles is, therefore, more suitable.

Decision by design team: floor plans of the office block and the factory block will be drawn separately on A1 size sheets at a scale of 1:50.

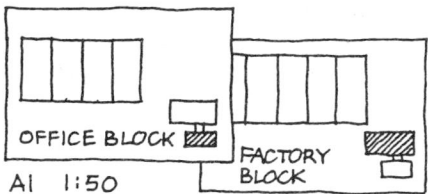

The A1 sheet size has already been chosen for floor plans. It is sensible to keep all drawings within a group the same size and the A1 size is suitable for all other location/general arrangement drawings.

It is necessary for some of the assembly and component details for this building to be drawn at 1:5 which is too large for A4 size sheets. Some of the roof and stair details will not fit conveniently on A3 size sheets without a risk of fragmenting the information. Both A1 and A2 size sheets would be suitable. The architect and structural engineer prefer to distinguish by sheet size between location and detail information and so opt for A2 size sheets. The services engineers expect to have very few detail drawings so opt for the A1 size sheets throughout their drawings.

Decision by design team: all location/general arrangement drawings will be drawn on A1 size sheets. Architects' and structural engineers' assembly and component drawings will be on A2 size sheets. Services engineers' detail drawings will be on A1 sheets.

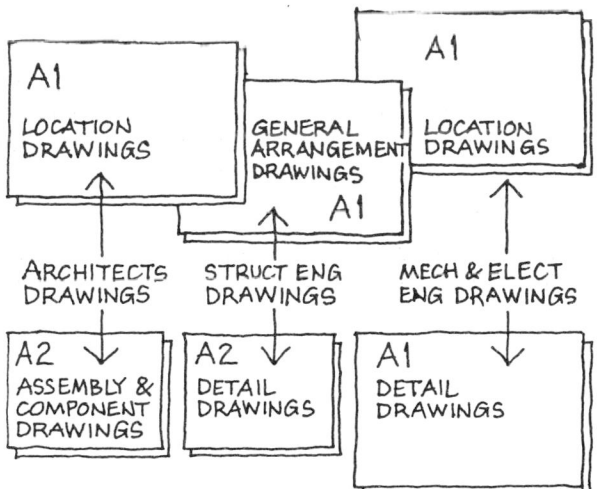

The decisions taken so far relate to all drawings and give the whole set a co-ordinated format. Final choices of drawings arrangement and numbering can differ between the separate sources and are made as follows:

5.4 Architect's drawings

The complexity of the detailing and the use of an A2 sheet size will result in more than a hundred assembly drawings. Some further grouping of the assembly set is, therefore, essential. The architect wants to ensure that the groups will suit the way the contractor might organise the project workload, particularly in relation to sub-contracts. The likely major sub-contracts are roofing, ceilings, external works and manufacture of doors and windows.

Decision by architect: the assembly drawings will be divided into groups representing parts of the building or site. The groups will comprise drawings whose main subjects are wall, stairs, roofs, openings, ceilings, fittings and external works.

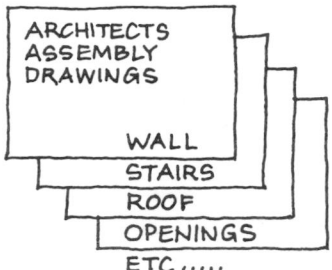

Although there will be about fifty component drawings, they all relate to purpose made windows and doors and are all referred to from the location drawings and schedules.

Decision by architect: the component drawings need not be divided into smaller groups.

Some of the schedules, in particular the openings schedules, will carry many references to assembly and component drawings. It is, therefore, important that these schedules can be retrieved easily.

Decision by architect: there will be a separate schedules group of drawings.

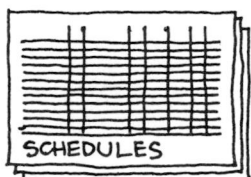

To assist in the search for information and to aid clear referencing between drawings it is helpful if the drawing numbers reflect the logic of the drawings arrangement. The sub-division of the assembly drawings can be identified in the drawing numbers by using blocks of numbers or by a simple code.

Decision by architect: the location, schedule, assembly and component groups will be identified by using drawings numbers starting with L, S, A and C as appropriate. The assembly drawings sub-groups will be identified by using blocks of numbers.

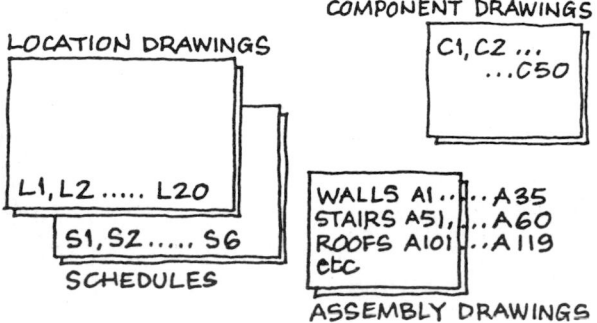

5.5 Structural engineer's drawings

The structural design entails both steelwork and reinforced concrete and a variety of detailing. As a result there will be about eighty drawings in the structural engineer's set. Location, assembly and component groupings will break the set down considerably but it is also important to note that the steelwork drawings will be required by the steelwork sub-contractor to prepare his fabrication drawings. It is sensible, therefore, to separate the steelwork and reinforced concrete drawings. Similarly, the piling will be let as a separate contract and this suggests a group of foundation drawings.

Decision by structural engineer: the drawing groupings in the structural engineer's set will have a location, assembly, component format. The location drawings will comprise separate groups of foundations, RC floors and steelwork layout drawings. The assembly drawings will comprise separate groups of RC details and steelwork connection drawings.

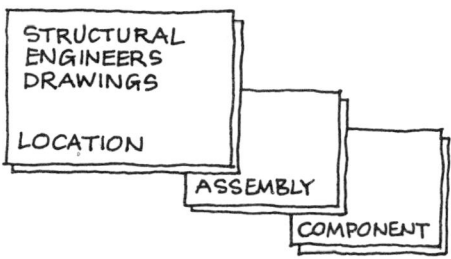

In numbering the drawings, the aim is to reflect the drawings arrangement and distinguish the drawings from those produced by the architect and services consultants.

Decision by structural engineer: the drawing numbers will start with L, A and C as appropriate with allotted blocks of numbers starting at 500.

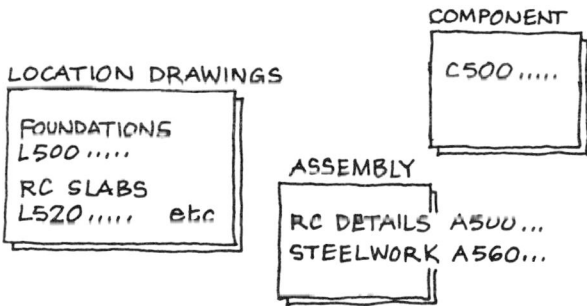

5.6 Services engineers' drawings

Unlike the architect's and structural engineer's drawings, the services engineers' drawings come from more than one source. This naturally creates groups relating to the office of origin of the drawings. In the cases of public health and internal transportation, the numbers of drawings are so few that further subdivision is unnecessary.

The mechanical and electrical services are quite complex and spread over the whole building and will require thirty and twenty three drawings respectively. Subdivision of the groups is, therefore, probably worthwhile but the relatively small numbers of drawings involved suggests that there is no need for an elaborate grouping. The requirement to show the engineering systems on plans and sections points to subdivision in terms of general arrangements and details.

The sequential design approach to co-ordination of some parts of the building will create about ten combined services drawings and these are seen as a separate group.

Decision by services engineers: the services engineers' drawings will be arranged in terms of office of origin. Where appropriate, the origin groups will be subdivided into layouts, schematics and details.

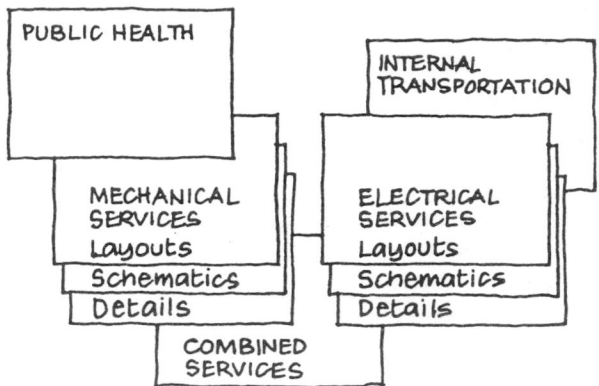

It will assist in identifying the type of service which is the subject of a drawing if the drawing number is coded appropriately and sub-groups are recognisable from the numbering.

Decision by services engineers: the drawing numbers of the services set will be alpha-numeric. The 'alpha' part will relate to the service type; the 'numeric' part will be sequential but in blocks of numbers where appropriate.

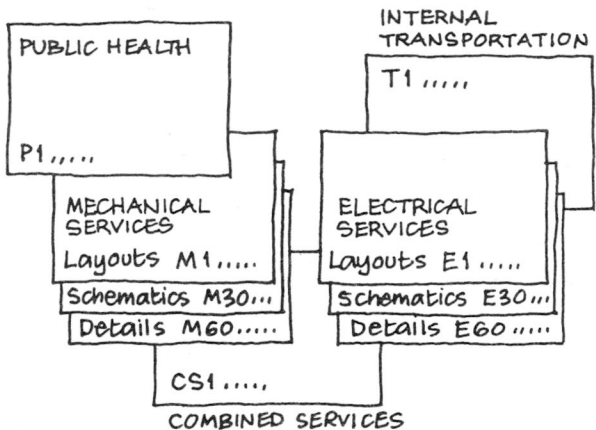

An analysis of the final set of design team production drawings is given in Figure 5.

5.7 Specialist contractors' drawings

In this example the tender documents will require that all production drawings and their arrangement should follow this Code. Each specialist will be required to provide an initial approximate schedule of production drawings giving sheet sizes and numbering for approval by the design team. The use of specialist contractors conveniently allows grouping by office of origin (page 15).

The plumbing and mechanical services sub-contractor produces different sets of drawings for different site trades. Mnemonic letters are used to distinguish plumbing – PS, mechanical – MS and duct work – DS. The letter 'S' distinguishes the specialist contractors' drawings from the consultants' drawings. Each of the three groups (PS, MS, DS) contains more than twenty drawings so sub-grouping is used as shown on page 32. Other drawings originate from mechanical services specialists for controls, air handling units and chillers. These are small sets which will not need subdividing as they can be identified by their office of origin and have a simple numerical sequence. Also, whilst not normally considered helpful, these small numer-

GROUPING	NUMBERING	SHEET SIZE	SCALE
ARCHITECTS DRAWINGS (204)			
Location (20)	L1,L2 ... L20	A1	1:100, 1:50
Schedules (6)	S1, S2 ... S6	A1	—
Assembly (128)			
Walls (35)	A1, A2 ... A35	A2	1:10, 1:5
Stairs (10)	A51, A52 ... A60	A2	1:10, 1:5
Roofs (19)	A101, A102 ... A119	A2	1:10, 1:5
Openings (30)	A151, A152 ... A180	A2	1:10, 1:5
Ceilings (13)	A201, A202 ... A213	A2	1:10, 1:5
Fittings (10)	A251, A252 ... A260	A2	1:20, 1:5
External works (11)	A301, A302 ... A311	A2	1:10, 1:5
Component (50)	C1, C2 ... C50	A2	NTS, 1:5
STRUCTURAL ENGINEERS DRAWINGS (84)			
Foundations (15)	L500, L501 ... L514	A1	1:50
RC Slabs (10)	L520, L521 ... L529	A1	1:50
Steelwork layouts (8)	L550, L551 ... L557	A1	1:50
RC Details (20)	A500, A501 ... A519	A2	1:10, 1:5
Steelwork connections (19)	A560, A561 ... A578	A2	1:10, 1:5
Components (12)	C500, C501 ... C511	A2	1:10, 1:5
SERVICES ENGINEERS DRAWINGS (81)			
Public health (12)	P1, P2 ... P12	A1	1:200, 1:100, 1:50
Mechanical services			
Layouts (15)	M1, M2 ... M15	A1	1:50
Schematics (10)	M30, M31 ... M39	A1	NTS
Details (5)	M60, M61 ... M64	A1	1:20, 1:5
Electrical services			
Layouts (16)	E1, E2 ... E16	A1	1:50
Schematics (4)	E30, E31 ... E33	A1	NTS
Details (3)	E40, E41, E42	A1	1:5
Internal transportation (6)	T1, T2 ... T6	A1	1:50, 1:10
Combined services (10)	CS1, CS2 ... CS10	A1	1:20

Figure 5 – Analysis of the final set of design team production drawings

ical sequences can be made unique for reference purposes by using the specialist's own project number as an affix (e.g. 1286/3).

The total number of electrical services drawings exceeds twenty so the mnemonic ES and blocks of numbers are used. The fire alarms, switchgear and lighting fittings are produced by specialist suppliers whose small sets of drawings are treated in the same way as those for controls, air handling units and chillers.

The drawings for the lifts, precast concrete panels, furniture and automatic sunshades are again in small sets and therefore will be treated similarly.

An analysis of the final set of specialist contractors' production drawings is given in Figure 6.

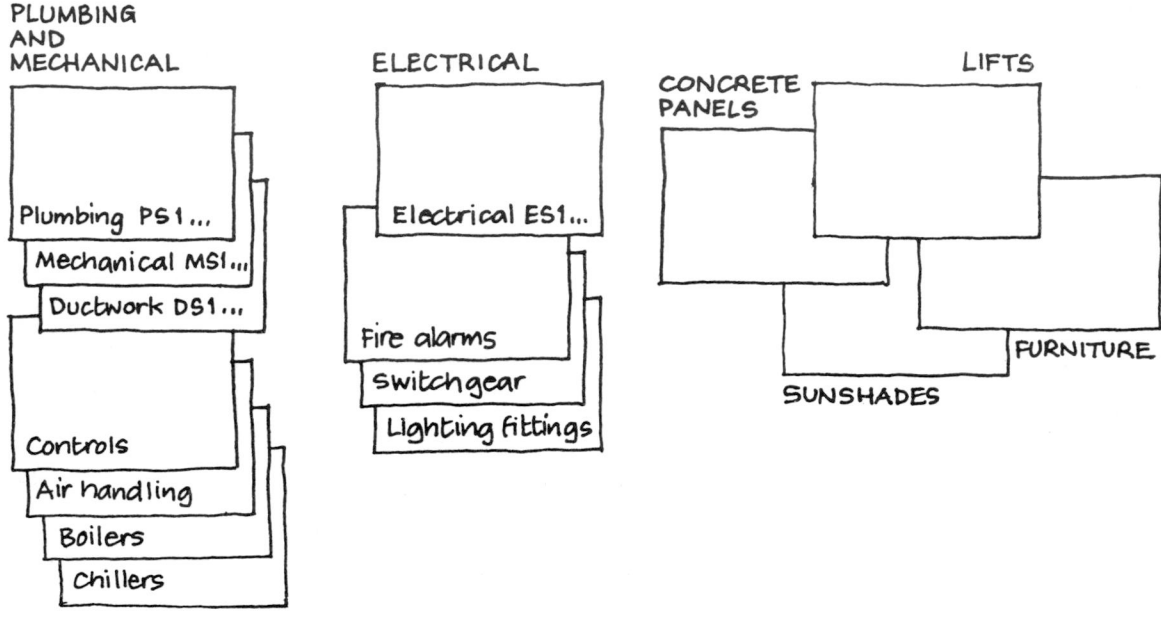

GROUPING	NUMBERING	SHEET SIZE	SCALE
PLUMBING AND MECHANICAL			
Sanitary services (14)	PS 1 ... PS 14	A1	1:200, 1:50, 1:5
Water and fire services (9)	PS 20 ... PS 28	A1	1:200, 1:50
Mechanical piped services (17)	MS 1 ... MS 17	A1	1:50
Plant rooms, mechanical services (7)	MS 20 ... MS 26	A1	1:20
Mechanical services details (12)	MS 50 ... MS 61	A1, A3	1:20, 1:5
Ductwork standard details (6)	DS 1 ... DS 6	A3	1:20, 1:10
Ductwork layouts (19)	DS 20 ... DS 38	A1	1:50, 1:20
Controls diagrams and schematics (12)	4826/1 ... 4826/12	A1, A4	NTS
Air handling unit details (8)	11847/1 ... 11847/8	A1, A4	1:20, 1:10
Boiler details and diagrams (4)	1286/1 ... 1286/4	A1, A4	1:20, NTS
Chiller details and diagrams (3)	3014728/1 ... 3014728/3	A1, A3	1:50, NTS
ELECTRICAL			
Schematic drawings (4)	ES 1 ... ES 4	A1	NTS
Lighting and power layouts (12)	ES 10 ... ES 21	A1	1:50
Auxiliary services layouts (9)	ES 40 ... ES 48	A1	1:50
Fire alarm layouts (9)	ES 60 ... ES 68	A1	1:50
Fire alarm details (5)	743/1 ... 743/5	A1, A3	1:50, 1:10
Switchgear details, diagrams (6)	47006/1 ... 47006/6	A3	1:10, NTS
Lighting fittings (6)	18804/1 ... 18804/6	A1	1:5
LIFTS			
Details, diagrams (14)	812003/1 ... 812003/14	A1, A3	1:20, 1:5, NTS
PRECAST CONCRETE PANELS			
Layouts, details (7)	253/1 ... 253/7	A1, A2	1:50, 1:20, 1:5
FURNITURE			
Details (20)	867/1 ... 867/20	A3	1:5
AUTOMATIC SUN SHADES			
Layouts, details, diagrams (10)	902/1 ... 902/10	A1, A2	1:50, 1:5, NTS

Figure 6 – Analysis of the final set of specialist contractors' production drawings

6 Drawings content

6.1 General

This section gives guidance on drawing content and the division of information between drawings and the specification. Research has identified where inadequacies of content are most likely to occur – see figure 7.

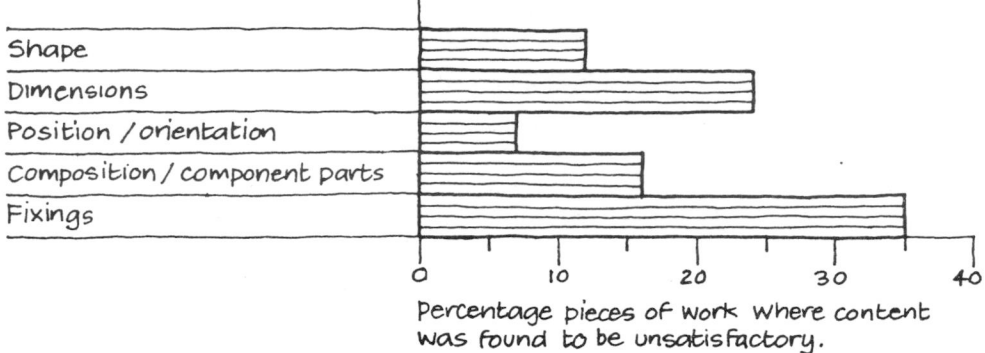

Percentage pieces of work where content was found to be unsatisfactory.

Figure 7 – Adequacy of information:
(From BRE examination of 30 sets of drawings, specifications and bills of quantities from sources considered to be producers of 'better than average' project information.)

The wide variety of building projects makes it impossible to give detailed check-lists of drawings content but when decisions on content are being made points to be considered are:

- The basic drawing types and their usual content
- Annotation
- Drawing referencing.

6.2 Drawing types and their content

For any particular piece of work the drawings will need to give information about:

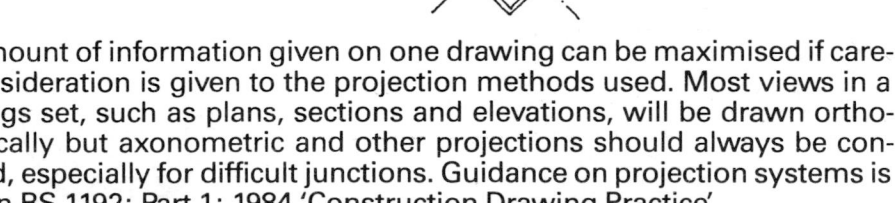

- Shape
- Dimensions
- Position/orientation
- Composition/component parts
- Fixings.

The amount of information given on one drawing can be maximised if careful consideration is given to the projection methods used. Most views in a drawings set, such as plans, sections and elevations, will be drawn orthographically but axonometric and other projections should always be considered, especially for difficult junctions. Guidance on projection systems is given in BS 1192: Part 1: 1984 'Construction Drawing Practice'.

Quite often the information about one piece of work has to be spread over several drawings. The danger, apart from failing to supply the information at all, is that errors may occur through too much fragmentation or too much repetition of the information relating to a particular part of the building. This danger is difficult to avoid but it can be minimised if the purposes of the main drawing types are observed.

Location or general arrangement drawings

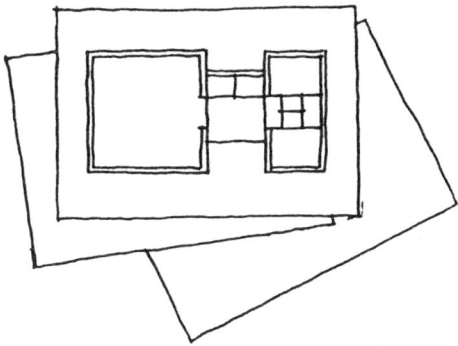

Location or general arrangement drawings should enable users to:

- gain an overall picture of the shape, layout and form of construction of the building/site;
- determine setting out dimensions for the building and site as a whole;
- locate and identify the spaces and parts of the building, e.g., rooms, doors, structural frame members, services terminals;
- pick up references which lead to more specific information.

Assembly drawings or detail drawings

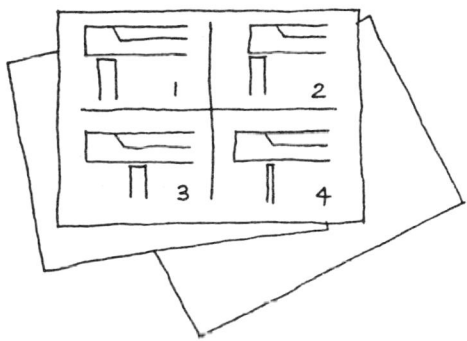

Assembly drawings or detail drawings should enable users to:

- determine how parts of the building are constructed and how they meet at junctions;
- pick up references to other detailed information.

Component drawings or detail drawings

Component drawings or detail drawings should:

- show the shape, dimensions and assembly of separate parts;
- identify and give information about components which cannot be given adequately on the assembly drawings.

Schedules

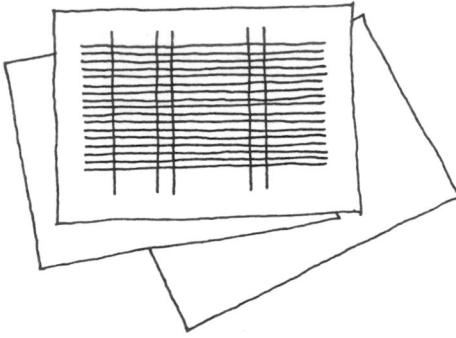

Schedules should:

- collect together repetitive information about similar parts of the building which occur in variety;
- give references to more detailed drawings where appropriate.

6.3 Annotation

General

The production drawings generally give information about size, shape and location of the various materials and components but these have to be identified by annotation in order to make the drawings intelligible.

Location of specification information

If substantial specification information is given on the drawings, or in the quantities and/or schedules, the danger of discrepancies and divergences will be increased. There is also a risk that some of it will be overlooked. The danger will be much reduced if the descriptions on the drawings and in the quantities are kept short. Also, avoidance of repetition will help to keep the quantities brief and avoid the drawings becoming crowded with information.

The inclusion of substantial specification information on drawings and in quantities and schedules can have an adverse effect on pre-contract procedures. If the descriptions are long, it is necessary to finalise the project specification in detail at an early date. On the other hand if the descriptions are kept brief, annotation of the drawings and preparation of the measured item descriptions can proceed on the basis of an outline specification. The full specification can then be completed while the other documents are being finalised. With a tight pre-contract programme the difference can be important.

It is therefore recommended that full specification information is normally given only in the project specification. Greater predictability and freedom from discrepancy will usually result if drawings, quantities and schedules, *identify* the different kinds and qualities of work, but do not aim to *specify* them. This can be achieved by using a few carefully chosen words with, as appropriate, a reference to the relevant part of the specification, e.g. 'Damp proof course F30/030. Such disciplined separation of graphic, scheduled, measured and specification information assumes and depends on the documents being arranged and cross-referenced in a way which makes it easy to read them together. This is the primary objective of CAWS and both the project specification (or specification preambles) and the quantities should follow this arrangement to ensure effective co-ordination and cross-referencing.

Written information on drawings

Repetition of written information on drawings is often the cause of poor co-ordination because, when making amendments, it is difficult to ensure that all affected drawings are changed. Ideally, written information should be given only once in a set of drawings. In practice, where drawings contain a number of different views of the same piece of work, some repetition of written information is unavoidable. However, if the set of drawings has been carefully planned and arranged, problems arising from amendments will be minimised.

Because of the variety of views of the same piece of work which occurs in a drawings set it is not practical to give hard and fast rules as to where and when annotation is necessary. Written information should only be put on drawings for good reason. There are only three good reasons:

- Because it is information which the drawing has specifically been produced to supply.
- Because the information is necessary to locate the view in relation to the building or site as a whole.
- Because the information is necessary to ensure easy and correct interpretation of the view.

Written information should not be put on a drawing simply because it is information which the designer has to hand.

What to include

The contractor will have to take account of all the information supplied in the project specification (or specification preambles). However, the site staff often only require sufficient information to allow them to retrieve the appropriate materials and/or components from the site store.

Good annotation, therefore, provides sufficient information to answer the following questions:

- What is it? e.g. wallplate.
- What is it made of? e.g. sawn softwood.
- Has it any important features? e.g. treated.
- What size is it? e.g. 100 × 50 mm.
- What is the CAWS reference to locate more specification information? e.g. G20/102.

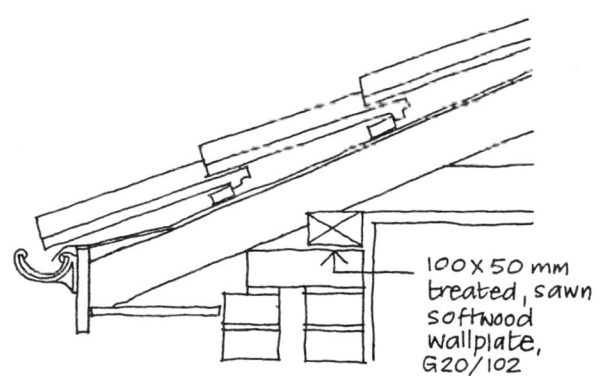

100 × 50 mm treated, sawn softwood wallplate, G20/102

The annotation '100 × 50 mm treated sawn softwood wallplate G20/102' then fulfils users' needs. The rest of the specification information such as type of treatment and type of softwood can be found by following up the reference. In some circumstances the amount of annotation on drawings can be reduced. Graphic conventions, such as standard brickwork hatching, can obviate the need for some of the description as can the use of schedules in the specification which might, for instance, list information about where each type of brickwork or mortar is to be used.

Drawing referencing

Drawing references should direct attention to a particular sheet and preferably to a particular view on that sheet. Imprecise referencing such as 'see engineer's drawings' or 'to be read in conjunction with all relevant drawings' are of little or no use. Ease of use and confidence in the information are more likely to result if the references display a logical pattern of links between the drawings in a set. The following should be taken into account when deciding on a referencing pattern:

- Almost all references should lead from the general to the particular, e.g. from location drawings to assembly or component drawings.

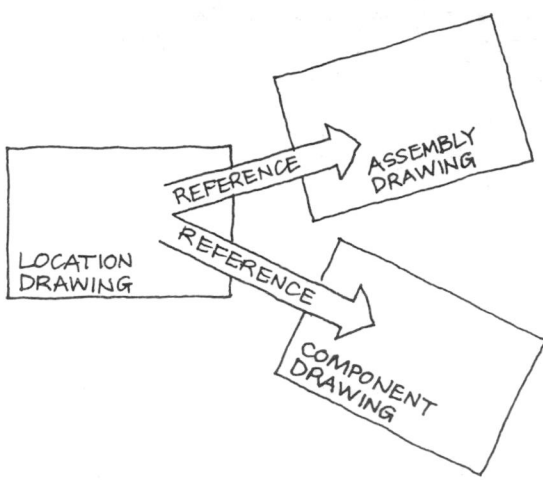

- References to more detailed information can conveniently be supplied on location drawings (plans, elevations etc). If, however, the building has a variety of design detail for similar features, it is usually best to route references through schedules. Using schedules in this way reduces the risk of omitting references but care must be taken in compilation since scheduled information is notoriously inaccurate.

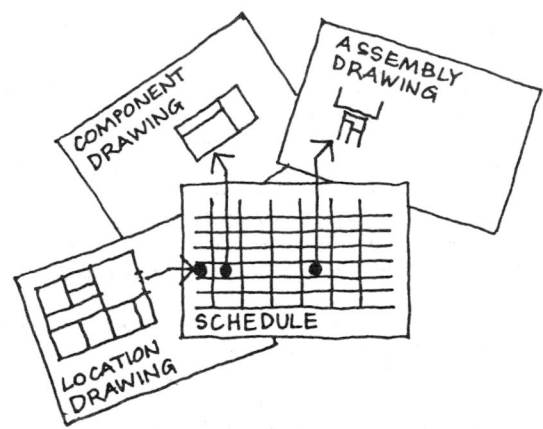

7 Planning, preparing and issuing the drawing set

7.1 Introduction

This section provides a guide to the essential stages of planning, preparing and issuing production drawings. For ease of reference a key to the stages is given in Figure 8.

In practice, the stages will sometimes have to overlap or alternate to suit the particular pre-tender programme. Some stages will need provisional decisions which can be made firm when subsequent related decisions have been taken.

Stage		Actions
7.2	Preparation	Check completeness of design information Prepare an outline schedule of drawings
7.3	Resources	Determine the resources required
7.4	Arrangement	Determine the arrangement of the drawings set
7.5	Format	Determine the format of the drawings set
7.6	Resource deployment	Decide on the manner of drawings preparation
7.7	Drawings schedule	Prepare schedule of drawings
7.8	Co-ordination/ production techniques	Determine requirements resulting from chosen technique e.g. copy negatives
7.9	Content	Decide drawings content in relation to drawings purpose
7.10	Draughting time	Determine man hours to produce each drawing
7.11	Programme	Prepare drawings programme Prepare drawings in accordance with drawings programme
7.12	Drawings register	Prepare drawings register and issue to all parties using the drawings
7.13	Issuing and revising	Devise a system for issuing and revising drawings
7.14	User guide	Provide 'user guide' to explain the arrangement and content of the drawings set

Figure 8 – Key to the stages

7.2 Preparation

Programming

Ideally, all design information should be substantially complete before the preparation of production information is begun. However, it is possible to overlap to some extent the detail design and the preparation of production drawings (stages E and F, Appendix 2). The state of completion of design should be reviewed so that areas where information is incomplete can be identified and completion of any outstanding design work included in the drawings programme. When preparing such a programme it is important to:

- Consider the requirements of the project in terms of input from:
  Client or building user
  Consultants
  Contractor
  Sub-contractors
  Supervision staff
  Statutory authorities.
- Include for the completion of the project specification and provision of information to the quantity surveyor. Ideally the specification should be in advanced draft form (if not final form) before final drawings are prepared. More commonly the specification will be finalised in parallel with the final drawings.

The preparation of drawn information, the specification and the quantities may be planned so that packages of information can be provided for the quantity surveyor on agreed dates. For example, the foundation drawings and the specification sections covering excavation, hard filling and concrete can be produced as an early package. This allows the production information to overlap the preparation of quantities, so shortening the pre-contract period.

Outline schedule of drawings

When the effect that design stage output will have on the production drawings has been determined the needs of the drawings users should be considered. The essential question is: 'For which parts of the building will drawn information be required?' The answer marks an important point in the development of the production drawings since it is the first indication of the amount of drawn information to be provided and will form the basis for later decisions on the format of the set. At this early stage it will usually be inappropriate to prepare anything like a firm drawings list: an outline schedule of drawing subjects should suffice. The preparation of this schedule is simplified if an office 'parts of the building' checklist which reflects the work of the office is available. Such an office checklist can be developed from a standard classification (Figure 9) or can be based on experience. The result of this stage will be an outline schedule of drawings, an extract from which is shown in Figure 10.

7.3 Resources

From the outline schedule of drawn information an assessment should be made of the overall draughting work load. If applicable, a preliminary assessment of the split between manual and computer draughting will need to be made.

To the draughting time must be added the time required to obtain and process information. This aspect is often underestimated; time studies indicate that the time taken for draughting and gathering information is approximately the same.

Using experience in conjunction with target times in the project plan of work, a rough profile of the project workload can be prepared. This will show where peak demands for resources and special requirements, such as the need for particular expertise, will occur.

Summary		Site layouts General arrangement drawings
Substructure		Excavation Floor beds Foundations Pile foundations
Structure	Primary	External walls Internal walls Floors and galleries Stairs and ramps Roofs Frames
	Secondary	External wall openings Internal wall openings Floor openings Balustrades Suspended ceilings Roof openings
	Finishes	External wall finishes Internal wall finishes Floor finishes Stair finishes Ceiling finishes Roof finishes
Services	Mainly piped and ducted	Refuse disposal Drainage Hot and cold water Gases Refrigeration Space heating Ventilation and air conditioning
	Mainly electrical	Power Lighting Communications Transport Security
Fittings	Fixtures	Circulation General room Culinary Sanitary Cleaning Storage
	Loose equipment	Circulation General room Culinary Sanitary Cleaning Storage
External		Substructure Structure Finishes Services Fittings

Figure 9 – Parts of the building checklist

(Based on CI/SfB Table 1 reproduced by kind permission of RIBA, UK licensee Ltd.)

BUILDING PARTS	NOTES	DRAWINGS
Floors and galleries	2nd to 4th repeated layout Mezzanine	4 plans
Stairs and ramps	3×2 type conc. 6 type timber	2 GA's, 4 details 1 GA, 2 details
Roofs	Upside down details as DHSS job	1 plan 6 details (standard)
Frame	Co-ord with struct.eng.	8 details
External wall openings	6 window types Auto entrance doors	Window schedule 20 details 7 component dwgs
	standard linings Five checks	Door schedule 10 details

Figure 10 – Outline schedule of drawings

The outcome of this analysis will be a broad understanding of the work force required including the need for temporary staff and for how long, the intended use of computer draughting and the need to reserve an appropriate amount of time for information gathering and clerical services. A reconciliation with the funds available (fee apportioned) for this phase can then be undertaken, taking account of any additional funding for special duties, such as co-ordination drawings.

7.4 Arrangement

Determine the arrangement of the production drawings to suit office practice, type of project and user needs (see Sections 3 and 5).

7.5 Format

Determine the format of the production drawings by choosing suitable sheet sizes, scales, drawing numbers and titles (see Section 4).

7.6 Resource deployment

In Stage 7.3 preliminary decisions were taken on the make-up of the draughting team and the extent of manual and/or computer draughting. At that stage the decisions were based very largely on the project timetable, the outline schedule of drawings and experience of similar types of work. Since then the choice of arrangement and format for the drawings have helped to identify the extent and complexity of the draughting task. Consequently, firmer decisions on the resource deployment can now be taken. It is important to make these decisions at this point in the planning because:

- from this point on there will be documents to prepare which will require some involvement from the draughting team, e.g. the drawings schedule, sketches, the drawings programme;
- the ability and experience of the individual members of the draughting team will influence the allocation of work and programming of drawings production.

42

7.7 Drawings schedule

At this stage the outline schedule of drawn information can be converted into a full schedule of the drawings to be prepared (see Figure 11). The following information has already been determined and can be recorded in the schedule:

- Drawing groupings (usually evident from the drawing numbering)
- Drawing numbers
- Drawing titles
- Scales
- Sheet sizes.

Space should be allowed for the following information which is necessary to complete the schedule:

- Man days for preparation of each sheet
- Notes (relating to such items as special content, importance of the drawing, relevance to other purposes etc).

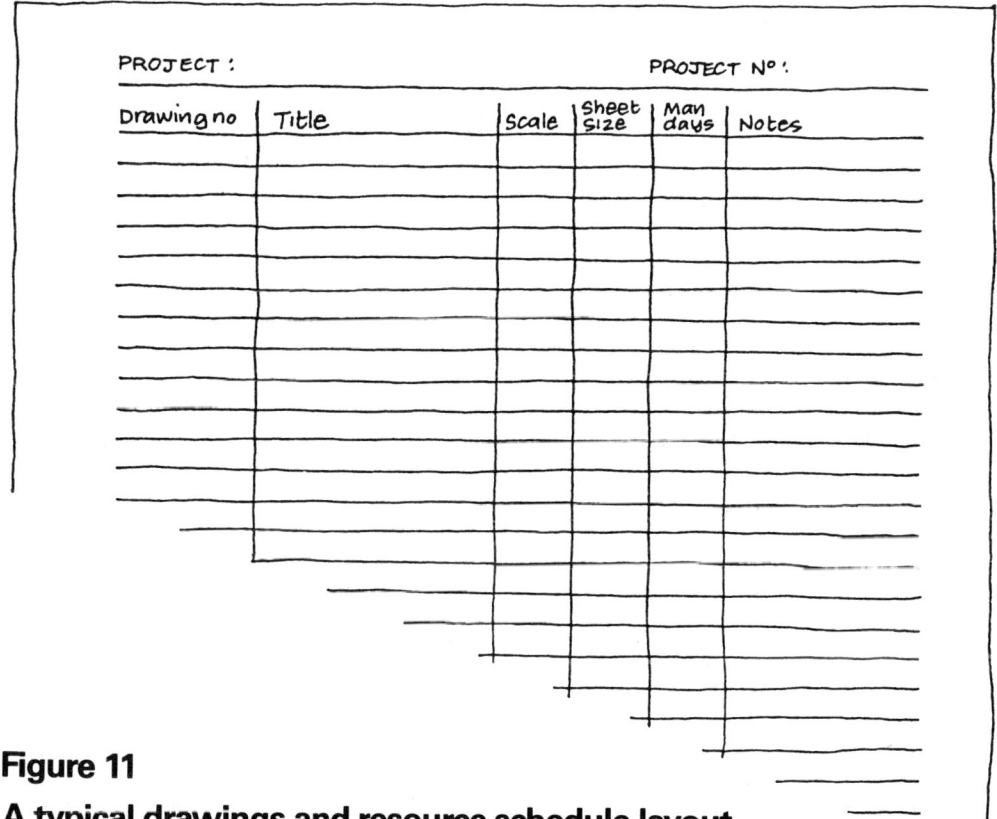

Figure 11

A typical drawings and resource schedule layout.

7.8 Co-ordination and production

Various drawings based co-ordination techniques are discussed in detail in Section 2. These techniques can also facilitate the preparation of the production drawings if they are chosen to suit the particular project and office resources.

7.9 Drawings content

At this stage the drawings required have been identified. It is now necessary to decide in detail what information each of these drawings should contain. General guidance on content can be found in Section 6.

The best approach is to prepare rough freehand sketches or 'cartoons', approximately to scale, which illustrate the drawing numbers and titles together with a list of the information they should carry. Some examples are shown in Figures 12 and 13.

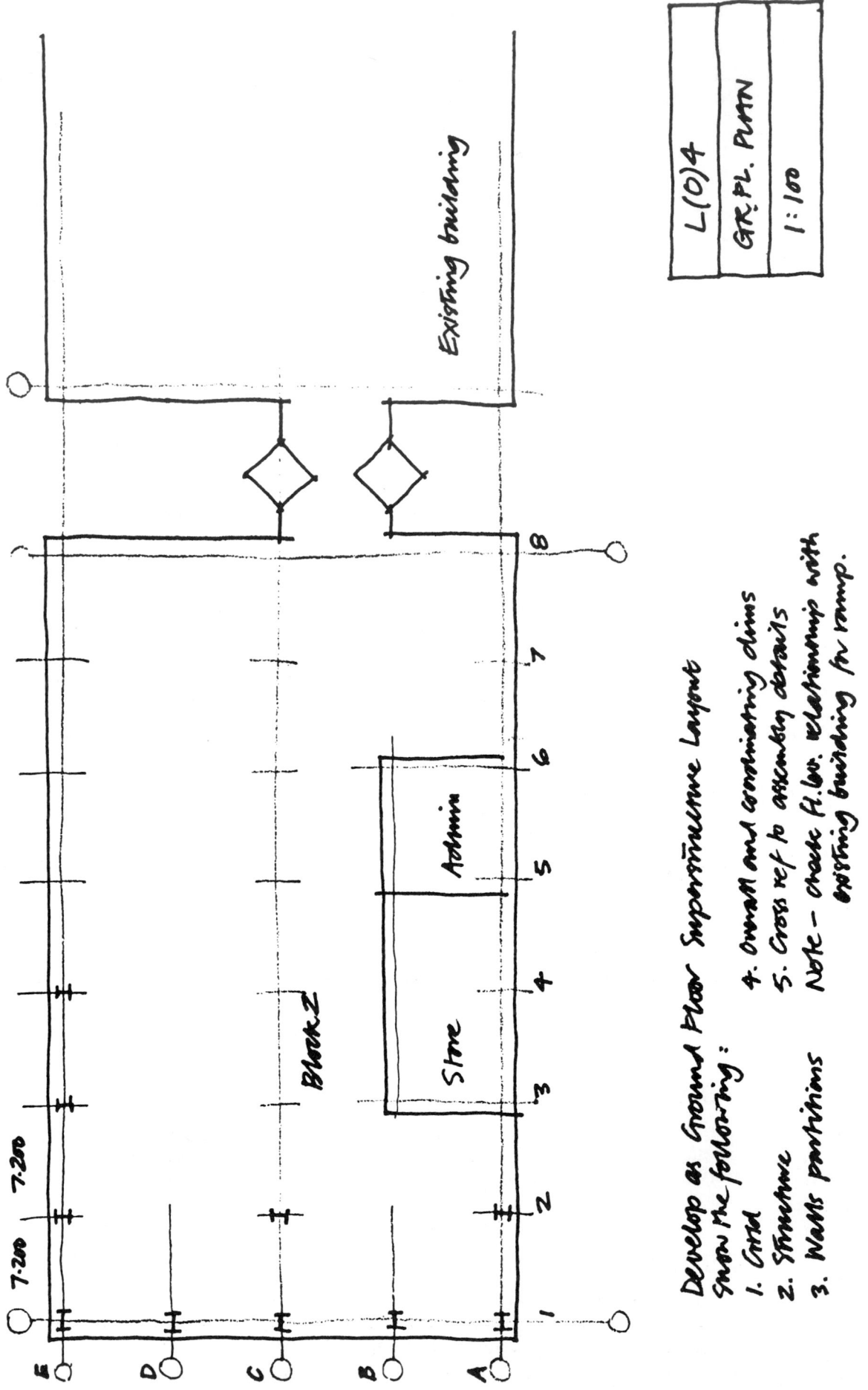

Figure 12 – Typical cartoon

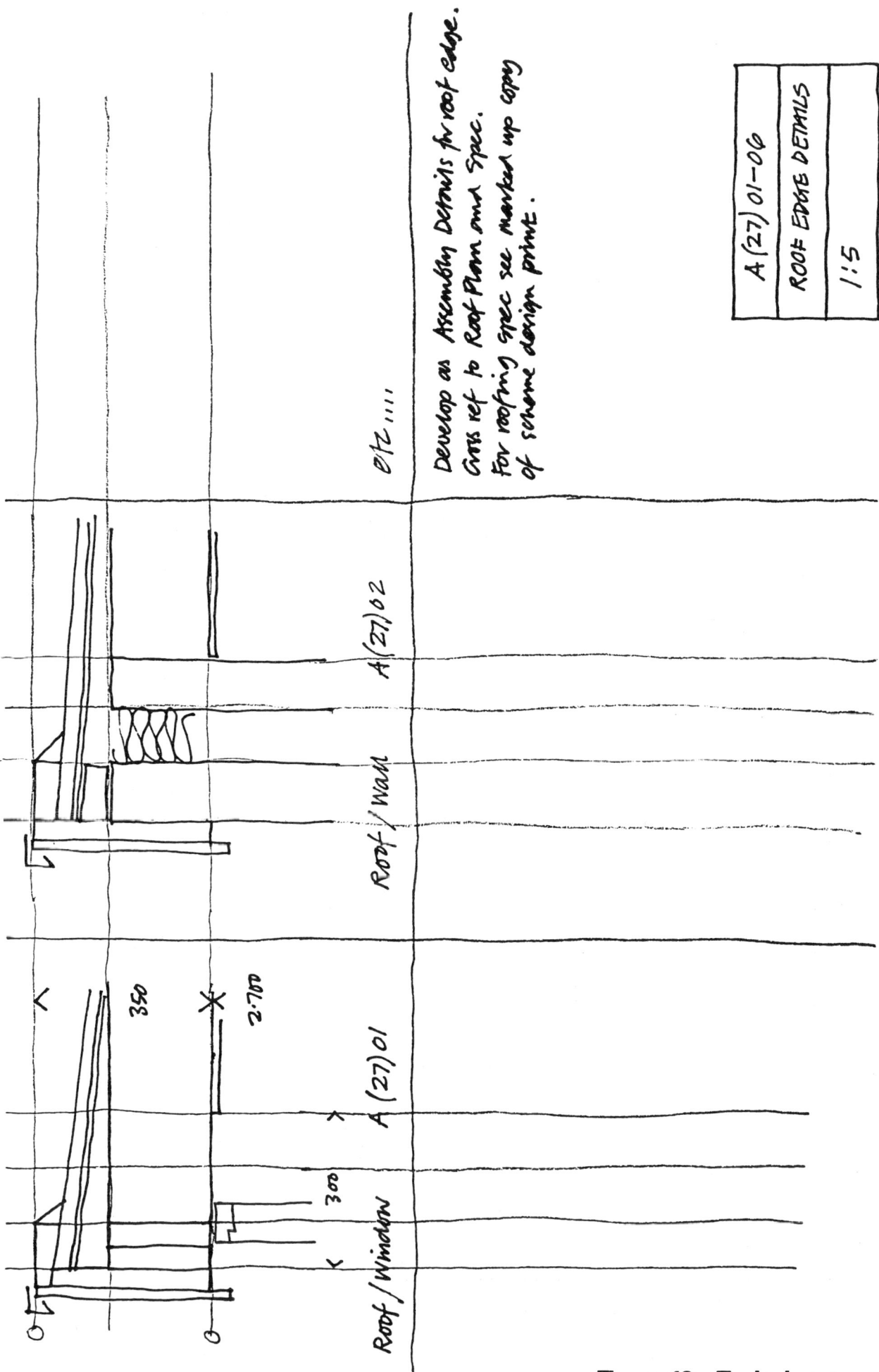

Figure 13 – Typical cartoon

45

7.10 Draughting time

Assessing the time of drawings preparation largely depends on experience and feedback from completed work. The assessment in man days should be determined for a particular drawing or a group of drawings and should allow for information gathering, checking and co-ordination as well as draughting time. The resultant times should be marked on each 'cartoon' as a target time for that drawing and added to the drawings schedule as a basis for the preparation of the drawings programme.

7.11 Programme

Each design discipline should prepare a drawing programme compatible with the overall design team programme (Figure 14). It should take the form of a bar chart similar to Figure 15.

For each drawing programme there are six stages of preparation. These are:

- **List the drawings**
  Sometimes individual drawings will be identified separately, particularly the main location or general arrangement drawings. Sometimes drawings which have similar content can be grouped together – most often these will be assembly or detail drawings.

- **Allocate the duration**
  Enter on the programme the man days allocated for producing each drawing or collection of drawings. This should be available from the drawings schedule and will include a time allowance for activities such as research, checking and co-ordination.

- **Assess the start and finish points**
  For each drawing or collection of drawings the earliest start time and the latest completion time should be established. These should take account of dependencies between the drawings of all design disciplines and of priorities such as deadlines for producing copy negatives. The time between earliest start and latest finish is indicated by a single horizontal line.

- **Decide who should prepare which drawings**
  Make a preliminary choice of who is best suited to do which drawings and pencil in the actual durations (the 'bars') based on earliest start.

- **Plot the resource histograms**
  Pencil in a preliminary resource histogram calculated from the 'bars'.

- **Level the resources**
  Redistribute the durations ('bars') to achieve the best compromise between resources and information production.

Once developed, the programme should be discussed and agreed with the rest of the design team. At this stage it is important to check that the programme still fits in with the resourcing decisions made earlier (Stage 7.3).

During the preparation of the drawings, it is important that all members of the design team are kept fully informed of progress so that they are always aware of their own position and their own deadlines.

Desk top microcomputers and relevant software packages are widely available for such simple bar chart programmes. Resource levelling is included and revision or update is a simple operation.

7.12 Drawings register

Once the production drawings have been prepared the drawings schedule can be converted into the drawings register. This will form the basis for the management of the completed production drawings set.

Each consultant should produce his own register but the project leader (usually the architect) should hold a drawings register which includes all of the

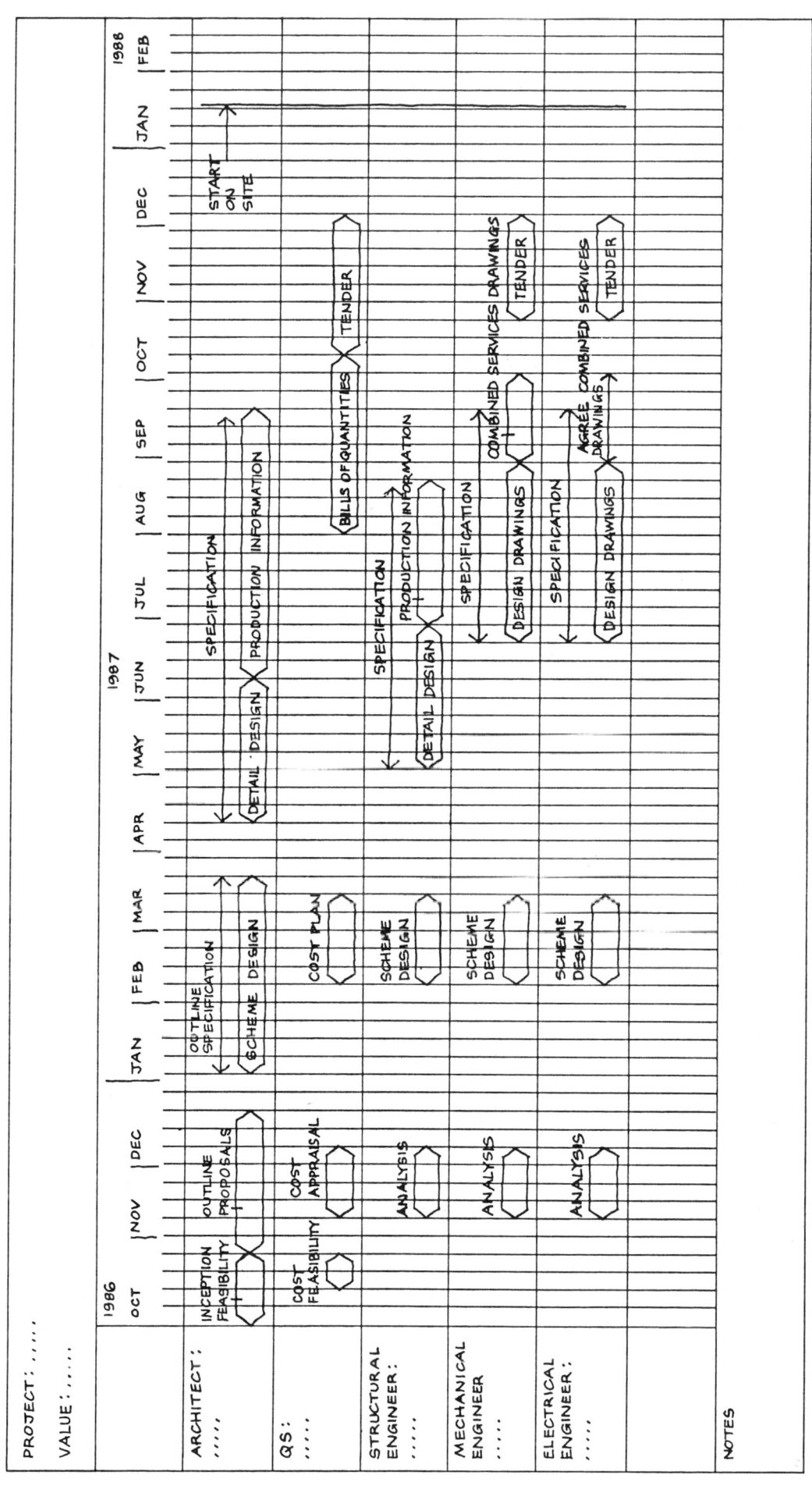

Figure 14 – Design team pre-contract programme

47

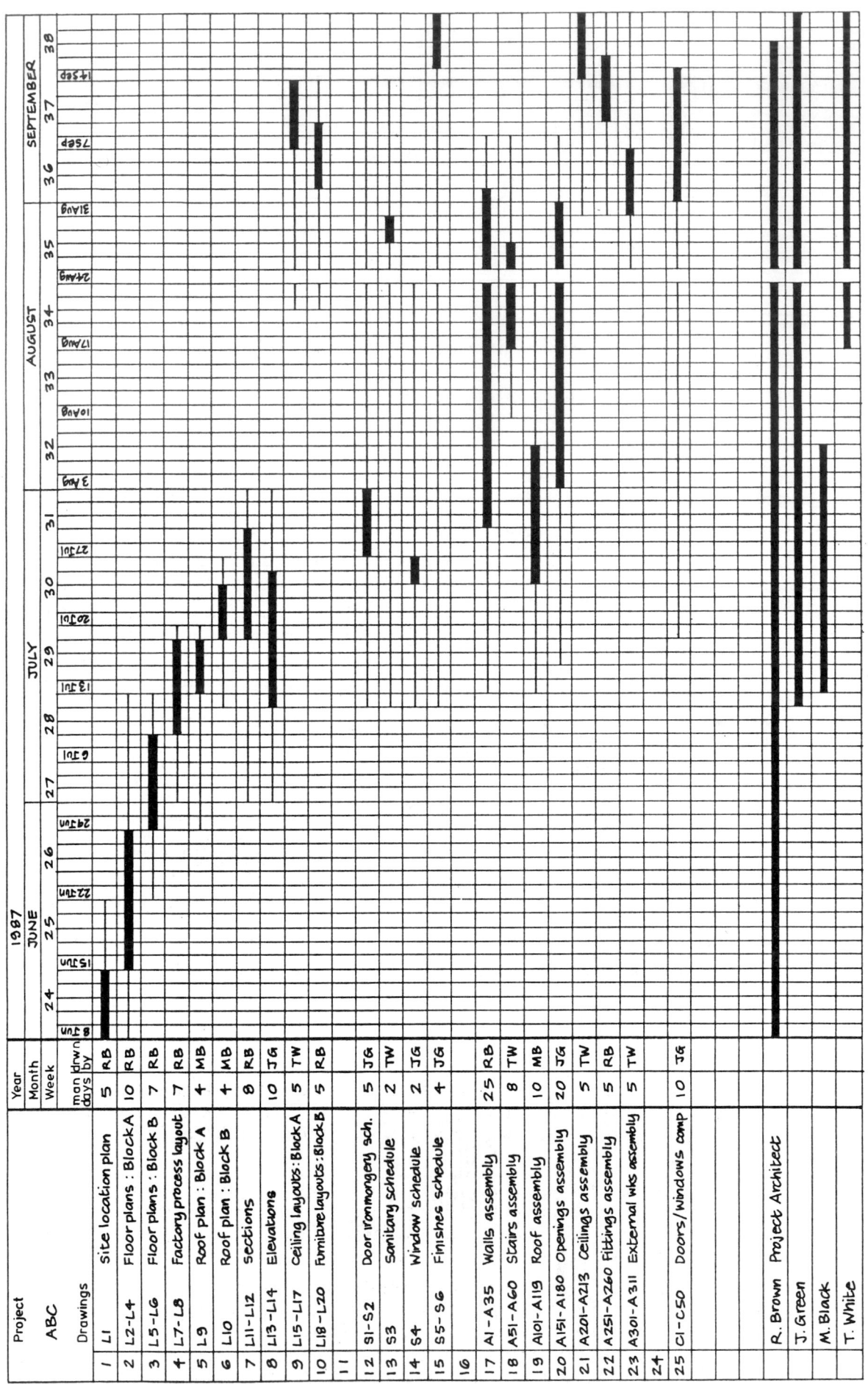

Figure 15 – Architect's drawing programme

project production drawings. This should be issued to everyone who is to use the drawings and should be updated regularly.

When amendments occur they should be recorded on the drawings register and all drawings users notified so that they can add the information to their registers.

An example of a typical layout for a register is shown in Figure 16.

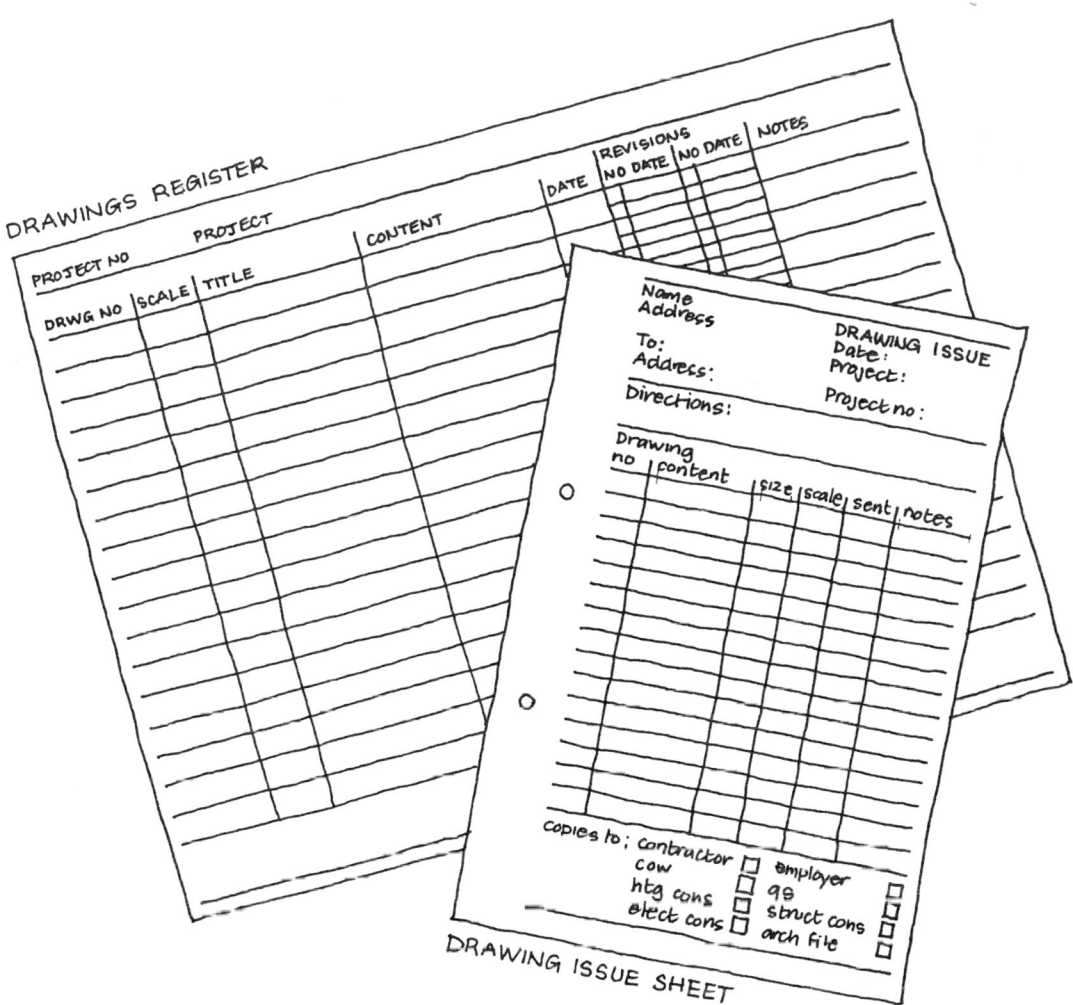

Figure 16 – Drawings register and drawing issue sheet

7.13 Issuing and revising

Not all users require a full set of drawings but the consequences of failing to supply the necessary drawings at the right time can be serious. It is important, therefore, that drawings are distributed to users in an organised fashion.

The easiest approach is to go through the drawings register checking each drawing off against a list of the drawings users for the project. This should be recorded on a spare copy of the drawings register and referred to whenever amendments are distributed.

BS 1192: Part 1: 1984 'Construction Drawing Practice' recommends that for amended drawings *'a short description of each revision should be provided under consecutive revision letters within a space adjacent to the title panel. The date of completion of the revision and the name or initials of the person effecting the revision should be stated. Wherever feasible, some means should be used to identify the location of the most recent revisions, for instance, by circling the locations in pencil on the back of the negative of amended sheets'.*

In addition, it is important to ensure that all the drawings affected by a revision are brought up to date as soon as the change has been agreed.

If any new drawings have to be prepared after the first issue of the production set, they should follow the arrangement and format of the initial set in order to retain the advantages of easy storage and retrieval. Whenever new or revised drawings are issued they should be accompanied by a record of drawings included and a copy of the record should be kept for reference. A typical example of a recording form is shown in Figure 16.

7.14 User guide

Users cannot be expected to recognise and understand without explanation all aspects of the arrangement and contents of a set of drawings. If full benefit is to be derived from the care and effort of the design team in organising and presenting the production drawings then some form of written 'users' guide' is essential. It should be short, illustrated by examples and limited to the important aspects of arrangement, format and content, and users should be made aware of its existence.

8 Drawn information at tender stage

8.1 General

This section gives guidance on drawn information to be issued to tenderers. It covers contracts with and without quantities, sets out the definitions and rules relating to drawn information in the Seventh Edition of the Standard Method of Measurement of Building Works (SMM7) and gives guidance on how those requirements may be satisfied.

8.2 Contracts with quantities

Prior to tender stage drawn information is used mainly for the measurement of quantities. On 'with quantities' contracts SMM7 requires drawn information to be provided to tenderers to give:

- an overall picture of the project to allow assessment of the cost significance of the design and make decisions about methods of construction.
- detailed information about parts of the work where this information is more effectively communicated graphically rather than by a lengthy description in the bill of quantities.

The requirements for provision of this information are dealt with in detail below. Drawings selected from those normally available for construction of the project should satisfy the SMM7 requirements (except for dimensioned diagrams).

Apart from the specific requirements for provision of drawings, SMM7 allows descriptive and specification information to be given on drawings or in the specification provided a specific cross reference is given in the bill of quantities description of the item (SMM7 General Rule 4.2).

The following types of drawings are referred to in SMM7:

- Location drawings
- Component drawings
- Dimensioned diagrams.

Location drawings

The SMM7 rules for Preliminaries/General conditions require certain location drawings to accompany the bill of quantities. These are defined in General Rule 5.1 as follows:

'Location drawings:
(a) Block Plan: shall identify the site and locate the outlines of the building works in relation to a town plan or other context.

(b) Site Plan: shall locate the position of the building works in relation to setting out points, means of access and general layout of the site.

(c) Plans, Sections and Elevations: shall show the position occupied by the various spaces in a building and the general construction and location of principal elements.'

The architect's smaller scale location drawings will normally satisfy this requirement.

The majority of work sections in SMM7 commence with a statement of the information to be provided specifically for that type of work. The requirements will normally be met by the architect's location drawings referred to above. If not, other drawings produced by the architect, structural, mechanical and electrical engineers etc should be provided. Figure 17 is a checklist of all SMM7 requirements for provision of location drawings.

SMM7 applies equally to all with quantities projects. However, when deciding which drawings to include to comply with the rules, the type, size and relative complexity of the particular project will need to be considered. For example the scope and location of foul drainage above ground (R11) for a simple single storey building may be adequately defined by the general arrangement floor plan showing the sanitary appliances whereas more detailed drawn information will be required for this work in a more complex building.

In addition to the requirements concerning location drawings there are other SMM7 rules, which although not specifically referring to drawings, can often be complied with to best advantage by giving information on drawings referenced from the bills of quantities. An example is Section D20 Excavating and filling which requires details of:

- Ground water level
- Trial pits or bore hole details stating their location
- Features retained
- Live over or underground services indicating location.

Component drawings

Component drawings are required by General Rule 5.2 to show the information necessary for the manufacture and assembly of components. Figure 18 is a checklist of all SMM7 requirements for provision of component drawings.

Dimensioned diagrams

Dimensioned diagrams are required by SMM7 General Rule 5.3 to show the shape and dimensions of the work covered by an item. They may be used at the discretion of the quantity surveyor as an alternative to a dimensioned description except in those cases where there is a specific requirement for a dimensioned diagram.

Dimensioned diagrams may be prepared by the quantity surveyor or, on his behalf, by the architect. They can also be extracts from the architect's or engineer's drawings reproduced at a suitable size for incorporation in the bills of quantities.

Dimensioned diagrams should not appear in documentation other than the bills of quantities. However, there may be occasions where it is more appropriate to issue the architect's or engineer's drawings with the bills of quantities rather than produce dimensioned diagrams. In such instances it will be necessary to identify the drawings in the bill description.

Preparation of tender documents

The tender documentation will include the bills of quantities, the tender drawings, the project specification (as appropriate), the form of tender and the letter of invitation. The bills of quantities will list the drawings from which the bills have been prepared, and copies of these should be kept as a record. It is good practice to indicate which of the drawings listed accompany the tender documents.

As much of the drawn information as possible should be contained within the bills of quantities to minimise the problem of expensive reproduction of drawings. The provision of copy negatives or similar methods rather than prints will also assist in keeping down tendering costs.

It will be of assistance to contractors if, when domestic sub-contractors are named in bills of quantities, the drawings and the specification relevant to their work are sent to them direct, obviating the need for all tendering contractors to do so when they can see from the bill that this has been done.

8.3 Contracts without quantities

Tender documentation for contracts without quantities will comprise the specification, all the architect's production drawings and, when applicable, those of the engineers. All the drawings necessary for the contractor to prepare his tender should be included and listed in the specification. In the case of services engineer's drawings these may be restricted to the design drawings, the remaining production drawings being part of the tender. Additional copies of the drawings should be included as considered relevant.

Figure 17 – Location drawings required to accompany the bills of quantities

SMM7 Section		Drawn information to be provided

A   Preliminaries/General conditions

		Location drawings required to accompany the bills of quantities: – Block plan – Site plan – Plans, sections and elevations The full definition of these drawings in given in the text above.

The information required to be provided in connection with the following work sections is to be shown either on the above mentioned location drawings or on further drawings which accompany the bills of quantities. The exception to this is drawn information marked * where specific location drawings are to be provided.

C   Demolition/Alteration/Renovation

C10	Demolishing structures	Location and extent of existing structures to be demolished.
C20	Alterations – spot items	Scope and location of the work relative to the existing layout indicating existing structure.
C30	Shoring	As C10
C40 C41	Repairing/Renovating concrete/brick/block/stone Chemical dpcs to existing walls	Scope and location of the work relative to the existing layout indicating existing structure.
C50 C51 C52	Repairing/Renovating metal Repairing/Renovating timber Fungus/Beetle eradication	Scope and location of the work.

D   Groundwork

D20	Excavation and filling – excavating	Location drawing* showing pile sizes and layouts.
D30 D31 D32	Cast in place concrete piling Preformed concrete piling Steel piling	Location drawing* showing: – General piling layout. – Position of different types of piles. – Position of the work within the site and of existing services. – Relationship to adjacent buildings.
D40	Diaphragm walling	Location drawing* showing: – Arrangement of diaphragm walls and their relationship to surrounding buildings. – Depths, lengths and thicknesses of diaphragm walls.
D50	Underpinning	Location and extent of the work and details of the existing structure to be underpinned.

Figure 17 (continued)

E	In-situ concrete/Large precast concrete	
E10	In-situ concrete	Relative position of concrete members, the size of members, the thickness of slabs and the permissible loads in relation to casting times.
E11	Gun applied concrete	Relative position of gun applied concrete members and the permissible loads in relation to casting times.
E20 E30 E31 E42	Formwork for in-situ concrete Reinforcement for in-situ concrete Post-tensioned reinforcement for in-situ concrete Accessories cast into in-situ concrete	As E10
E50	Precast concrete large units	Details of precast members showing stressing arrangements and full details of anchorages, ducts, sheathing and vents. Relative positions of concrete members, the size of members, the thickness of slabs and the permissible loads.
E60	Precast/Composite concrete decking	Relative positions of concrete members, the thickness of slabs and the permissible loads. Details of purpose-made, prestressed concrete members showing stressing arrangements and full details of anchorages, ducts, sheathing and vents.

F	Masonry	
F10 F11 F20 F21 F22 F30	Brick/block walling Glass block walling Natural stone rubble walling Natural stone/ashlar walling/dressings Cast stone walling/dressings Accessories/Sundry items for brick/block/stone walling	Plans of each floor level and principal sections showing the position of and the materials used in the walls. External elevations showing the materials used.
F31	Precast concrete sills/lintels/copings/features	As E50

G	Structural/Carcassing metal/timber	
G10 G11 G12	Structural steel framing Structural aluminium framing Isolated structural metal members	Position of work in relation to other parts of the work and of the proposed buildings. Types and sizes of structural members and their position in relation to each other. Details of connections or of the reactions, moments and axial loads at connection points.
G20	Carpentry/Timber framing/First fixing	Scope and location of the work.
G30 G31 G32	Metal profiled sheet decking Prefabricated timber unit decking Edge supported/Reinforced woodwool slab decking	Extent of the work and its height above ground level. Size of units where not at the discretion of the Contractor.

Figure 17 (continued)

H	Cladding/Covering	
H10	Patent glazing	Scope and location of the work.
H11	Curtain walling	
H12	Plastics glazed vaulting/walling	
H13	Structural glass assemblies	
H30	Fibre cement profiled sheet cladding/covering/siding	Extent of the work and its height above ground level.
H31	Metal profiled/flat sheet cladding/covering/siding	
H32	Plastics profiled sheet cladding/covering/siding	
H33	Bitumen and fibre profiled sheet cladding/covering	
H40	Glass reinforced cement cladding/features	As E50
H41	Glass reinforced plastics cladding/features	As H30
H50	Precast concrete slab cladding/features	As E50
H51	Natural stone slab cladding/features	Scope and location of the work.
H52	Cast stone slab cladding/features	
H60	Clay/concrete roof tiling	Extent of roofing work and its height above ground level.
H61	Fibre cement slating	
H62	Natural slating	
H63	Reconstructed stone slating/tiling	
H64	Timber shingling	
H70	Malleable metal sheet prebonded coverings/cladding	Extent of roofing work and its height above ground level including the location and spacing of all laps, drips, welts, cross welts, beads, seams, rolls, upstands and downstands.
H71	Lead sheet coverings/flashings	
H72	Aluminium sheet coverings/flashings	
H73	Copper sheet coverings/flashings	
H74	Zinc sheet coverings/flashings	
H75	Stainless steel sheet coverings/flashings	
H76	Fibre bitumen thermoplastic sheet coverings/flashings	
H	Work to existing buildings	Scope and location of the work relative to: – The existing layout indicating the existing structure. – The proposed layout.

Figure 17 (continued)

J	Waterproofing	
J10	Specialist waterproof rendering	Scope and location of the work.
J20	Mastic asphalt tanking/damp proof membranes	Plan of each level indicating the extent of the work and its height above ground level together with restrictions on the siting of plant and materials. Section indicating the extent of the tanking work.
J21	Mastic asphalt roofing/insulation/finishes	
J22	Proprietary roof decking with asphalt finish	
J30	Liquid applied tanking/damp proof membranes	
J31	Liquid applied waterproof roof coatings	
J40	Flexible sheet tanking/damp proof membranes	Plan at each level indicating the extent of the roofing work and its height above ground level together with the instructions on the siting of the plant.
J41	Built up felt roof coverings	
J42	Single layer plastics roof coverings	
J43	Proprietary roof decking with felt finish	
J	Work to existing buildings	Scope and location of the work relative to: – The existing layout indicating the existing structure. – The proposed layout.

K	Linings/Sheathing/Dry partitioning	
K10	Plasterboard dry lining	Scope and location of the work. Services located within the ceiling or partition where the work includes complex integral services.
K30	Demountable partitions	Scope and location of the work. Services located within the partition.
K31	Plasterboard fixed partitions/inner walls/linings	As K10
K32	Framed panel cubicle partitions	Scope and location of the work.
K33	Concrete/Terrazzo partitions	As E50
K40	Suspended ceilings	Scope and location of the work including integral fittings. Services located within the suspended ceiling void including any additional support for same.
K41	Raised access floors	Scope and location of the work.
K	Work to existing buildings	Scope and location of the work relative to: – The existing layout indicating the existing structure. – The proposed layout.

L	Windows/Doors/Stairs	
L	Work to existing buildings	Scope and location of the work relative to: – The existing layout indicating the existing structure. – The proposed layout.

Figure 17 (continued)

M	Surface finishes	
M10	Sand cement/Concrete/Granolithic screeds/flooring	Scope and location of the work.
M11	Mastic asphalt flooring	As J20
M12	Trowelled bitumen/resin/ rubber-latex flooring	Scope and location of the work.
M20	Plastered/Rendered/Roughcast coatings	
M21	Insulation with rendered finish	
M22	Sprayed mineral fibre coatings	
M23	Resin bound mineral coatings	
M30	Metal mesh lathing/Anchored reinforcement for plastered coatings	Scope and location of the work. Services located within the lathing, where the work includes complex integral services.
M31	Fibrous plaster	Scope and location of the work.
M40	Stone/Concrete/Quarry/Ceramic tiling/mosaic	
M41	Terrazzo tiling/In-situ terrazzo	
M42	Wood block/Composition block/ Parquet flooring	
M50	Rubber/Plastics/Cork/Lino/Carpet tiling/sheeting	
M51	Edge fixed carpeting	
M	Work to existing buildings	Scope and location of the work relative to: – The existing layout indicating the existing structure. – The proposed layout.

P	Building fabric sundries	
P30	Trenches/Pipeways/Pits for buried engineering services	Layout of the services.
P31	Holes/Chases/Covers/Supports for services	

Q	Paving/Planting/Fencing/Site furniture	
Q10	Stone/Concrete/Brick kerbs/edgings/ channels	Scope and location of the work.
Q21	In-situ concrete roads/pavings/bases	As E10
Q22	Coated macadam/Asphalt roads/ pavings	Scope and location of the work.
Q23	Gravel/Hoggin roads/pavings	
Q24	Interlocking brick/block roads/ pavings	
Q25	Slab/Brick/Sett/Cobble pavings	
Q26	Special surfacings/pavings for sport	
Q30	Seeding/Turfing	
Q31	Planting	
Q40	Fencing	Scope and location of the work. Location of fencing specially designed to suit sloping ground.

Figure 17 (continued)

R	Disposal systems	
R10	Rainwater pipework/gutters	Scope and location of the work.
R11	Foul drainage above ground	
R12	Drainage below ground	Layout of the drainage.
R13	Land drainage	

X	Transport systems	
	All sections	Scope and location of the works, including extent of work in motor machinery or plant rooms.

Y	Services	
Y10	Pipelines	Scope and location of the work including extent of work in plant rooms.
Y11	Pipeline ancillaries	
Y20–Y25	General pipeline equipment	
Y30	Air ductlines	
Y31	Air ductline ancillaries	
Y40–Y46	General air ductline equipment	
Y50	Thermal insulation	
Y52	Vibration isolation mountings	
Y53	Control components – mechanical	
Y60	Conduit and cable trunking	Scope and location of the work.
Y61	HV/LV cables and wiring	Scope and location of the work.
Y62	Busbar trunking	For final circuits:
		– Distribution sheet* setting out the number and location of all fittings and accessories.
		– Location drawing* showing the layout of the points.
Y63	Support components cables	Scope and location of the work.
Y70	HV switchgear	
Y71	LV switchgear and distribution boards	
Y72	Contactors and starters	
Y73	Luminaires and lamps	
Y74	Accessories for electrical services	
Y80	Earthing and bonding components	As Y61
Y92	Motor drives – electric	Scope and location of the work.

Figure 18 – Component drawings required to accompany the bills of quantities

SMM7 Section		Comment
F	**Masonry**	
F20	Natural stone rubble walling	Component drawings required for carvings and sculpture only.
F21	Natural stone/ashlar wallings/dressings	
F22	Cast stone walling/dressings	
H	**Cladding/Covering**	
H10	Patent glazing	
H11	Curtain walling	
H12	Plastics glazed vaulting/walling	
H13	Structural glass assemblies	
L	**Windows/Doors/Stairs**	
L30	Timber stairs/walkways/balustrades	A component drawing may be provided as an alternative to a dimensioned description.
L31	Metal stairs/walkways/balustrades	
N	**Furniture/Equipment**	
N10	General fixtures/furnishings/equipment	Applies only to fixtures, furnishings and equipment not associated with services.
N11	Domestic kitchen fittings	A component drawing may be provided as an alternative to a dimensioned diagram.
N12	Catering equipment	
N13	Sanitary appliances/fittings	
N15	Signs/notices	
N20 – N23	Special purpose fixtures/furnishings/equipment	
Q	**Paving/Planting/Fencing/Site furniture**	
Q50	Site/Street furniture/equipment	As N
X	**Transport systems**	
	All sections	A component drawing may be provided as an alternative to a description of type, size, pattern, capacity, etc.

Appendices

Appendix 1

Members of the Drawings Working Group and Consultants

BEC Representatives

Peter Jordan, CEng, MICE, FCIOB (Chairman)
Don Fidler, RIBA, DA, to October 1983
Richard Thairs, RIBA, MBIM, from October 1983

RICS Representatives

Christopher Willis, FRICS, FCIArb
Anthony Mothersdale, ARICS

RIBA Representatives

Paul Castle, BArch, RIBA
John Birch, RIBA
Margaret Elbogen, BA (Secretary)

ACE Representatives

Peter Campbell, JP, DIC, CEng, FIStructE, FICE, FIMarE, FIHT
Alan Foster, FCIBSE
Anthony Wallace, MA, FCIBSE, MASHRAE

PSA Representative

Hugh Gunnell

Consultants

David Crawshaw, BSc } Building Research
Keith Snook, BSc, MCIOB } Establishment

Adrian Michie, MCIBSE, MBIM, DMS } Building Services
John Hawley, BEng } Research and Information
David Jerdin, BSc, MSc, CEng, MInstE } Association

John Potter, RIBA } Architects
Richard Bulmer, DipArch, RIBA }

Appendix 2

Outline plan of work

Reproduced by permission of the RIBA

Stage	Purpose of work and Decisions to be reached	Tasks to be done	People directly involved	Usual Terminology
A. Inception	To prepare general outline of requirements and plan future action.	Set up client organisation for briefing. Consider requirements, appoint architect.	All client interests, architect.	Briefing
B. Feasibility	To provide the client with an appraisal and recommendation in order that he may determine the form in which the project is to proceed, ensuring that it is feasible, functionally, technically and financially.	Carry out studies of user requirements, site conditions, planning, design, and cost, etc., as necessary to reach decisions.	Clients' representatives, architects, engineers, and QS according to nature of project.	
C. Outline Proposals	To determine general approach to layout, design and construction in order to obtain authoritative approval of the client on the outline proposals and accompanying report.	Develop the brief further. Carry out studies on user requirements, technical problems, planning, design and costs, as necessary to reach decisions.	All client interests, architects, engineers, QS and specialists as required.	Sketch Plans
D. Scheme Design	To complete the brief and decide on particular proposals, including planning arrangement appearance, constructional method, outline specification, and cots, and to obtain all approvals.	Final development of the brief, full design of the project by architect, preliminary design by engineers, preparation of cost plan and full explanatory report. Submission of proposals for all approvals.	All client interests, architects, engineers, QS and specialists and all statutory and other approving authorities.	

Brief should not be modified after this point.

Stage	Purpose of work and Decisions to be reached	Tasks to be done	People directly involved	Usual Terminology
E. Detail Design	To obtain final decision on every matter related to design, specification, construction and cost.	Full design of every part and component of the building by collaboration of all concerned. Complete cost checking of designs.	Architects, QS, engineers and specialists, contractor (if appointed).	Working Drawings

Any further change in location, size, shape, or cost after this time will result in abortive work.

Stage	Purpose of work and Decisions to be reached	Tasks to be done	People directly involved	Usual Terminology
F. Production Information	To prepare production information and make final detailed decisions to carry out work.	Preparation of final production information i.e. drawings, schedules and specifications.	Architects, engineers and specialists, contractor (if appointed).	
G. Bill of Quantities	To prepare and complete all information and arrangements for obtaining tender.	Preparation of Bills of Quantities and tender documents.	Architects, QS, contractor (if appointed).	
H. Tender Action	Action as recommended in NJCC *Code of Procedure for Single Stage Selective Tendering* 1977.*	Action as recommended in NJCC *Code of Procedure for Single Stage Selective Tendering* 1977.*	Architects, QS engineers, contractor, client.	
J. Project Planning	To enable the contractor to programme the work in accordance with contract conditions; brief site inspectorate; and make arrangements to commence work on site.	Action in accordance with *The Management of Building Contracts* and Diagram 9.	Contractor, sub-contractors.	Site Operations
K. Operations on Site	To follow plans through to practical completion of the building.	Action in accordance with *The Management of Building Contracts* and Diagram 10.	Architects, engineers, contractors, sub-contractors, QS, client.	
L. Completion	To hand over the building to the client for occupation, remedy any defects, settle the final account, and complete all work in accordance with the contract.	Action in accordance with *The Management of Building Contracts* and Diagram 11.	Architects, engineers, contractor, QS, client.	
M. Feed-Back	To analyse the management, construction and performance of the project.	Analysis of job records. Inspection of completed building. Studies of building in use.	Architect, engineers, QS, contractor, client.	